BOWS IN THE CLOUDS

Mary McFadden

For my mother...

My Inspiration

Chapter 1

'Go on, Mary. Call for her.'

'But the Alsatians, they're barking. I'm afraid,' I replied angrily.

'Sure, they're chained in the yard. They can't get ya.'

We stood there, my friend Tara and I at the bottom of Alice's garden staring warily at the long path leading to the back door.

'Why don't you call up, Tara,' I said, looking sternly down at my friend. Tara is a lot smaller than me, even though she is only six months younger. I'm nine, and she will be nine in July.

'No way!' she retorted, shaking her head from side to side. 'I'm not going near those dogs.' She crossed her arms in front of her chest in a stubborn statement.

'But you want me to go, don't ya?' I sneered at her.

'Yes. You're the one who wants to show off your new cardigan, aren't ya?' she replied cockily.

I turned away from her in silence because this was true.

It was Easter Sunday, and we had just finished eating our Easter eggs. I was very keen to show our friend Alice my new yellow cardigan that my nana had knitted for me for Easter. I was so proud of it because it was beautiful. My cardigan had ribbons threaded through the cuffs, which lay frilly at the back of my hands, and beautiful shiny white buttons with a little yellow flower on each one. I loved my nana for knitting it for me.

We stood for a moment in silence.

'Never mind,' my friend Tara said. 'We will call some other time.'

My childish vanity overrode my fear of the dogs. I looked at Tara.

'I'm going up,' I said.

She stared back at me, wild-eyed with shock and fear. 'Okay,' she said nervously. 'I'll wait here for you.'

Off I went, walking slowly up the long tarmac pass to the back door, my wee heart jumping in my chest. I was holding my breath. 'They're chained,' I kept reassuring myself.

As I drew nearer to the garden shed, I could hear talk and laughter coming from the garden next to Alice's, and that calmed me a little knowing that someone was around if the dogs did get me. Slowly and quietly, I walked to the back door. I could see from the side of my eye that one of the Alsatians was chained to the fence to the left of the garden. I couldn't look.

I couldn't see the other dog, but I could hear him. He was locked in the shed to my right. The dogs were named Prince and Rex. Rex was not as vicious as Prince. Prince was always angry.

I was nearly there. My wee body was trembling. Only one more step and I was at the door.

Suddenly I could hear someone hissing to Prince. It was someone from the garden from next door.

'Go on, Prince. Get her.' *Hiss. Hiss. Hiss.*

I was very scared now. Why was someone doing that? I heard the chain being rattled. I was banging on the door with my fists. Prince was on my back, biting into my sides. I could feel the sharp stabbing of his teeth biting into my skin. My next recollection was opening my eyes to see the clear blue sky as I lay flat on my back in the garden. The other Alsatian dog, Rex, who had been in the shed to my right was walking back and forth across my torso as I lay there. I had fainted.

I don't recall what transpired immediately after that. I just remember Alice's mam holding my hand and walking me home.

I couldn't talk, but I do remember vividly looking down at the new yellow cardigan and being very sad because it was torn to shreds. This upset me - also, the look on my mother's face when she saw me.

She turned ashen white and started screaming at Alice's mother, 'What happened to her?'

I couldn't speak.

'These are very severe bites to your child, Mrs Tuite,' the doctor was saying to Mammy as he examined me. 'What age is she?'

'She is nine, Doctor.'

'Yes,' the doctor repeated. 'Very nasty! It's a miracle her lungs were not punctured. I'm going to make it my business to have those Alsatians put to sleep immediately. Maybe I should have her admitted to hospital?' I heard the doctor say to Mammy.

I instantly yelled, 'No, Mammy, don't let him put me in hospital!' I started to shake all over at the prospect of being sent there and being left alone, away from Mammy.

My mother was shocked at my outburst and took me onto her knee. 'Okay, Mary love. Calm down; I won't. Can you treat her here, please? She has been through enough today.'

My wounds healed well, although my mother had to bathe them and change my bandages quite often for a short time after. I had several bite wounds on both sides and one on the top of my bottom. I recall being very embarrassed when the doctor was examining that wound. I remember hoping to myself that my mammy wouldn't mention it to the doctor.

We lived on a council estate. The majority were working class, with large families. There were seven of us – four boys and three girls. I'm sort of in the middle, with two younger brothers. We were all very close and shared a great camaraderie. Everyone looked out for each other. It was comforting and safe.

But something changed inside me after the dog's attack. It had taken place only a few months ago, and I was starting to feel nervous and jumpy. I woke up in the mornings feeling fearful. That was new for me as I had been a fearless little girl. I would take on any challenge, but now, I was different. There was no long-lasting physical harm done to me from the attack, and the dogs were put to sleep, which was a good thing for them cause my eldest brother had been going to do it his way.

My friend Tara was always calling to me and asking if I was okay.

'I was scared, Mary, when I heard you screaming so I ran home to tell my mammy what was happening. I didn't know what else to do.' She quivered.

'I know, Tara. It's okay,' I reassured her. 'I'm fine now. Sure I would have done the same.' After the dog attack, my mother didn't allow me to call for Alice anymore, which was fine by me because any thoughts of going near that house again filled me with fear. My friend Tara stopped calling to her also. Their family and mine became somewhat estranged afterwards, and Alice made new friends, but we still greeted each other in passing.

There was always drama in our house and the biggest one soon after this was my father leaving us. I was ten years old. Being honest, I don't have many memories of him being there much anyway, and the times I do recall were not very happy ones. He was always drunk. I can probably remember three occasions in my childhood when he was sober, but they were very fleeting.

I don't know if my daddy was an alcoholic. My mother told me later in life that he'd never touched a drop for thirteen years of their marriage. My parents were married at the age of nineteen. I do know that my father was a good husband and hard worker early on in their married life. I have no memory of those years. I was too young. All I remember was the rows between him and Mammy every time my daddy would come home drunk. This fear, which seemed to creep into my life, would consume me. I'd become panicky, and my heart would jump in my chest.

Putting that aside, I loved it when Daddy came home. I wanted my daddy in my life. We all did. I envied other girls who had their daddy at home all the time. I missed him a lot when he was gone.

His visits became less and less frequent. We all knew that Daddy would be gone in the morning. When we would question Mammy about where Daddy was, her mood would seem to change. She'd look angry and would tell us abruptly that Daddy was working with our Uncle Pat, Daddy's brother, in England.

We stopped asking where Daddy was after a time because we sensed how upset Mammy would be when we did. We all simply carried on and adjusted to our daily lives.

Ironically, a strange thing happened to me about this time. One day while me and my younger brothers were sitting watching TV after school, a knock came at the door. My mammy answered.

She came into the sitting room. 'Mary,' she said. 'There are a couple of girls from your class at the door wanting to know will you go out to play.'

'What girls, Mammy?' I said curiously because I did not have many friends calling. Only my friend Tara or her brothers and sisters called.

'I don't know their names, love. Go to the door.'

This new frightening jump in my chest began as I went through the hall to the front door. My fear was realised as I stared at the faces of the girls there.

They were not in my class; they were in the other fifth-year class. There were too many pupils for one teacher so we had two fifth-year classes in our primary and these girls at my front door didn't even like me. I knew this because they were always teasing me in class.

'Hello, Susan. Hello, Anne,' I said almost in a whisper.

'Are ya coming out to play?' one of them asked loudly.

I didn't want to go out with them. I was afraid of them. 'No,' I stammered. 'I can't. My dinner will be ready soon.'

'Well, your mammy didn't say you couldn't go out,' Susan replied angrily.

My heart was thumping in my chest now, and I felt like I couldn't breathe. This fear, which was almost part of my daily life now, erupted inside. 'No, no,' I answered as I began to close the door. 'I can't go out now, sorry.'

I nearly had the front door closed, Susan pushed her face into the gap between the door, and the words she said stunned me speechless.

'I know where your daddy is,' she snarled at me. 'He lives with another woman, and they have children.'

I slammed the door.

I stood there for what seemed like an eternity staring into space, unable to comprehend what I had just been told.

I felt the same sensation that had hit me when the Alsatian attacked me a year ago; shock. My mammy's voice took me back to reality.

'Mary, are you there?'

'Yes, Mammy,' I replied in a croak.

I never repeated what Susan said to me to anybody until now. I tricked my mind into believing I'd never heard those words at all. It was the only way my young brain could process this heartbreaking, humiliating experience, but it shook me to the core emotionally.

One thing I did understand from that day forward was why my mammy changed when we mentioned Daddy's name, and I was so sad for her. I avoided Susan and Anne at school in the playground as much as possible after that. On the rare occasion when I would have to pass them by or stand in line with them close by, I'd keep my head down to avoid any eye contact with them. They never bothered me after that.

My sweet mother sacrificed and devoted her life to raising us kids alone mostly, except for my nana, who lived nearby and helped my mother as much as she could. We were poor. Women didn't get help financially from welfare back then. Looking back now, it must have been so hard for my poor mother to make ends meet. She never turned us against my daddy or even said a bad word about him to us our whole lives. She told me years later that she didn't want us to be bitter towards him for our sake. My mother is an amazing lady.

Thankfully the financial strain had been relieved somewhat this year, which was 1976. My two eldest brothers and my eldest sister had started working. My brothers Patrick and Ciaran had just been employed in a timber yard, and my oldest sister Lizzy was working in the corner shop on our housing estate. This income was a huge help to Mammy, and she seemed to laugh more.

We are all close in age with barely two years between us. This fact also contributed to our family togetherness. I spent most of my playtime with my two younger brothers, Joseph and Sean, and, of course, my friend Tara. She too has a big family – ten children in total – and like us, all close in age. Tara's mammy and mine were also close friends.

I always felt protective over my younger brothers and would frequently go up against boys in our street who picked on them. When we went out to the street to play, Mammy was always shouting after us: 'Mind your brothers!' or 'Mind your sisters!' as the case may be, so perhaps this was the reason for my protectiveness.

Added to that, I was a bit of a tomboy, where in contrast, my sister Erin, who is two years my senior, was what Mammy would refer to as a girlie-girl.

There had been many occasions when my mammy would explode in frustration when she saw me coming in from the street. 'Mary, look at you!' she would yell. 'Why can you not keep your clothes clean? You only left the house an hour ago, and you come back looking like you were dragged through a pig pen.'

I would look down at myself in silent response, totally unaware of my mud-stained clothes. 'What do you be doing, child? Your sister Erin never comes in from the street, mud from head to toe like you always do,' Mammy would rant on in frustration.

'I don't know, Mammy. I'm sorry. I was only playing hide and seek in the field.' Funny, as I sit here writing in my 52nd year of life and reflecting back on these times, I don't ever remember my sister Erin playing hide and seek in the field.

I loved school and loved learning. I always got top marks, particularly in English and spellings. I also loved books, and reading was my passion. Achieving the best results was of utmost importance in school on every subject. So, when suddenly, out of nowhere, this same year of 1976, I lost my concentration on every subject, I was devastated. It was like everything had been wiped out of my mind. I was still in my fifth year in primary school.

One day, the teacher gave us a small written test on Geography. It was easy, just naming counties in Ireland. I was looking at the page in front of me, terrified because I could not think of one answer. My mind was blank.

Previously, a little exam like this was the simplest thing in the world for me to do. I knew all the counties in Ireland by memory. I could also spell all of them off the top of my head. But, here I sat this day in class bewildered, in absolute despair.

'What is happening to me?' I thought.

My teacher came to my desk on her rounds. She looked at my blank page and saw that I had no answers written down. 'Mary, why have you no answers written down?' she asked me.

I couldn't answer her because I did not know what to say. My mind was blank. I was stunned beyond words. My teacher questioned me again. 'Mary,' she said. 'You know these answers. What is wrong with you?'

I looked up at her, and all I could say was, 'I forgot, Miss.'

She stared at me for a moment with a bewildered look on her face and then she left me to check the other girls' work.

I put my head down. The disappointment I felt at myself that I could not answer these simple questions was beyond words; frustration, anger and even sadness. All these emotions welled up inside me, but mostly, I was ashamed at myself. I had been a very confident little girl at school before that day. Now, that was gone. Writing here now in the present at age fifty-two, I just realised that the sad thing was, my confidence never returned in class for the rest of my school-going years.

I was to learn later in life about post-traumatic stress and delayed shock, but back then, I was just a frightened ten-year-old girl who was ashamed of herself because she had turned into a dope at school.

We were coming to the end of the school year and had only one more term in primary school left. Daddy had not been home in a while, which I was almost relieved about because I still held that memory of what had been told about my daddy and felt very angry; more for hurting Mammy than for leaving us.

My nana had become like a second mother to us after Daddy left. We all loved her dearly. She'd had her fair share of hardship and pain in her life.

Mammy was the youngest of five girls, two of whom had died at very young ages. Mammy's sister Lilly died when she was eighteen months old, and her other sister Edith died when she was twelve from polio. Edith was the closest in age to Mammy. My mother told me she used to sit at Edith's bedside and read to her when she was ill and bedridden. This was back in the 1940s. Mammy was never told what happened to wee Lilly. She told me that my nana never talked about it to her. All she heard was that Lilly went blue while sitting on my grandfather's knee.

My grandfather Patrick died when my mother was carrying me. Mammy was six months pregnant; that was in June 1966. Then in the late eighties, Mammy's older sister Cecilia, who lived in England died in her forties from an abrupt illness.

Despite the unimaginable heartache from losing her husband and three of her children, my nana had a smile and a song for everyone.

Nana had a brother living with her when we were young. His name was Paddy. He was a widower and never had children. He suffered a mild stroke and moved in with my nana to be looked after in his recovery.

Uncle Paddy used to take my sisters and me to the park on Sunday afternoons with his two dogs. Then we would have tea and buns at his house before he took us home. Uncle Paddy favoured me over my sisters and brothers. I don't know why. Perhaps because I was fiery and high spirited, this was a challenge for my poor mother, but Uncle Paddy seemed to get great amusement out of me. He would often give me small gifts; simple things like a balloon or a small doll, or a hairbrush, but the best gift I ever got from him was the white frilly umbrella.

My nana was visiting one day. She came into the small sitting room carrying a white umbrella. I heard her talking quietly with Mammy. She was reluctant to give me the umbrella. I heard her say to my mother, 'I don't know where Paddy got this dirty thing. I don't think

I should give it to Mary, Evie. It's filthy.'

My mother's name is Evelyn, but everybody calls her Evie for short.

On hearing this, I was out of my chair at the small table and over to my nana like a bolt of lightning.

'Nana, is this umbrella for me?' I blurted out. 'It's beautiful!'And to me it was beautiful. It had a pretty handle with little beads and a lovely lacey fringe around the edge. It didn't look dirty to me. It was my present from Uncle Paddy, and I would fight to the death to have it in my hands.

My nana sensed how happy and excited I was, so she relented and smiled at me as she handed me the umbrella. I heard her say to Mammy, 'Make sure you wash that before the child uses it.'

I was not interested in any conversation between my nana and Mammy after that. I had my beautiful umbrella, and nothing else mattered in my young world right then.

We lived in a two-story two-bedroom house. We had a small front room downstairs adjacent to another small sitting room, and a tiny kitchen, which three adults would fill. In those days, small kitchens like that were called sculleries. We had no finery or fancy furniture. We were poor but happy in our wee home.

So this posed a problem for me with my new umbrella. Where was I going to find space to put it up and sit under it or spin it around? Mammy would not let me put it up in the house anyway, and it was raining outside.

I used my imagination a lot as all children do. I loved to go to fantasy land in my mind. Sometimes I could make my fantasy land feel so real that I would believe I was there. I could be in that daydream state for hours. Obviously, I was a princess there. I had everything that I wanted, and all the girls I knew were jealous of me. I wanted so bad to be there now with my new umbrella.

As I sat there looking out at the rain, an idea came to my mind. I could sneak out to the back garden. My brothers and sisters wouldn't notice, and Mammy was busy upstairs gathering the laundry. Yes, my young mind was racing now. Even better, the rain would wash the dirt off my umbrella and then Mammy wouldn't take it off me to wash it.

I slipped past my siblings, who were watching TV. I was tall for my age but very thin and had a unique ability for sneaking around when I had to without being noticed. I very quietly lifted the latch on the back door; umbrella tucked under my arm. I went to the back of the small shed in our garden tucked my jumper under my bum, sat down, then opened my umbrella. 'Oh, this is just perfect,' I thought happily. Very soon after, I was in my favourite fantasy land once again. I just loved the sound of the rain as it bounced off my umbrella and the pretty fringe hung so perfectly. When the umbrella was up, I felt safe and protected. It was bliss.

'Where is Mary?' I could hear my mammy shouting. 'Mary? Mary? Where has that child gone now?'

All I remember after that was my umbrella being lifted from me and my mother taking me into the house by the hand. I heard her mutter, 'Damn Uncle Paddy and his umbrella.'

One winter evening soon after this, I came down from my room for tea, and I began to cough. The scary thing was I couldn't stop. With every breath I took, I would get a spasm of coughing. By late evening it was continuous. My mammy sent my older brother over to the doctor to get some cough medicine for me. The medicine did not work. It was getting late now, and I was tired. My cough was getting worse, so my mother sent my brother over to fetch my great aunty Lilly. Mammy always said that Aunty Lilly has the cure for all ailments.

'Maybe she has something lodged in her throat, Evie,' Lilly said to my mammy. 'I'll walk her around and see if it helps.' Lilly put her arm around me, singing her heart out.

Lilly was always singing, and Mammy told me that she believed song was the best cure in the world. Well, I'm sure that's true, but it didn't cure my cough.

'Go over and ask Mrs Daly, can you phone an ambulance,' Mammy said to one of my siblings.

My heart skipped a beat when I heard Mammy say that. I could feel myself tensing at the thought of having to go to hospital. Mammy knew this and came to me. She put me on her knee.

'Mary, don't be worried. I will stay with you the whole time,' she reassured me. I was too exhausted now to put up any argument.

When we got to the hospital, a doctor checked my chest with a stethoscope and then said to Mammy, 'Your daughter has croup.'

'What is that?' I wondered. By then, I just wanted to sleep.

'Does she sleep in a damp room?' the doctor questioned Mammy.

'No,' Mammy replied. 'It's cold in the winter, but her bed is warm. She has never suffered coughing like this before.' Suddenly, Mammy exclaimed, 'That damn umbrella!'

The doctor and I both stared at her. She then started to tell the doctor all about me disappearing out of the house in the rain and sitting on the wet ground behind the shed with my umbrella.

'Ah,' the doctor sighed.

I had to stay in the hospital for a week, and it was the scariest time in my young life. I missed my mother and siblings so much, being away from home. I cried myself to sleep every night. Poor Uncle Paddy got fierce verbal abuse from my nana. I never received any more presents from him after that!

Sixth class, the last year in primary. I didn't like school anymore; not like I used to. I was always anxious and nervous, living with a dread of something I can't put a name to. My concentration just seemed to have disappeared. I didn't have the enthusiasm for working out the answers to exams. It had all gone, and with it, my confidence.

I was a little afraid too because we had Sister Martina teaching us this term and everybody was talking about how wicked she was.

'She shouts at you and slaps your hand with a ruler if you misbehave,' I overheard a bunch of the girls from my class saying to each other.

I was very quiet at school. I never got involved with the gang, with the popular girls. Mostly it was just my friend Tara and I hanging about in the schoolyard. I was noticing now that I was starting to feel different from others, excluded somehow. I was growing envious of some of the girls in my class — the wealthy ones.

When I was clever in school, I was content with my young life, but now it was different. I carried shame with me every day, and I was always afraid and cautious. The mental block I had suffered with back in fifth class still haunted me. My grades dropped. I was still getting quite good school reports, but the As were fewer and the Bs and Cs greater in number, and this fear that hung over me like a black cloud constantly affected my ability to learn, and to achieve in my subjects the way I used to.

I hated this new me. I tried hard to force myself to be and act like I used to. Then some girl would laugh at me, and it just tore at me inside, so I became more and more quiet and withdrawn in class each day. It was not long until Sister Martina had sussed me out, though. She was wicked. She was small and had rosy red cheeks, and when she was giving out to us, her head would shake in frustration, her big jaws would be flopping from side to side. I used to think her face was going to explode if she didn't calm down.

We were studying history one day, and I was concentrating well. Sister Martina was reading a chapter aloud to the class, and we all had to read along from our books. Here I was in my comfort zone. I loved to read. I could capture the story so well. Nothing was going on around me when I was reading.

Suddenly, Sister Martina stopped reading. We all looked up at her. She seemed to be staring at me, I thought.

'Okay,' she said. 'One of you is going to read the next chapter aloud to the class.'

Well, that anticipation that I had long lost returned to me there and then. I could feel the blood rushing through me, and the adrenaline. I hoped with all my heart that it would be me.

'Mary!' Sister Martina shouted. 'I want you to read the next chapter. Read it out loud and clear for us all to hear.'

So, with a flutter in my chest, I stood up. This was my moment, and nothing could hurt me now. With slightly shaking hands, I began to read the whole chapter out loud. I could have read the whole book there and then with joy. When I finished, I looked up at Sister Martina. She seemed to be in a daze, like she was staring into my brain or something. I started to tense up in fear.

'Thank you, Mary. That was very good,' she said. 'You can sit down now.'

My buzz was over, but it was thrilling while it lasted.

I was still on my pink cloud when I got home from school that day. All the bad feelings had ebbed away. I was the happiest wee girl alive until…

'It's Daddy!' my sister and younger brothers were shouting from the hallway. 'Daddy!' There was a lot of excitement.

I looked for my mother. She was getting up slowly from her favourite armchair by the fire. She looked worried. I could see the frown on her face; Mammy's mood always changed when Daddy was around. She spoke sharply and seemed nervous, where ordinarily she was calm and easy going, and when I saw Mammy tense, I got afraid. I stayed by her side.

When Daddy came into the room though, my fear subsided. I became overwhelmed with joy when I saw his face. I ran to him and wrapped my skinny arms around his waist. We all did. Daddy was smiling and jolly swinging us around. It was wonderful.

Mammy did not greet him. She just stood by the fire looking on. Daddy dislodged us from him and walked closer to Mammy. Suddenly, my mother told us to go sit back down. 'Watch telly for a while,' she ordered. 'I need to talk to your daddy in the front room.'

'Daddy's drunk,' one of my brothers remarked.

I went quiet again. Fear rose once more.

Mammy came back into the sitting room shortly after. 'Children, go outside and play for a while,' she said. 'I will call you in soon.'

We were playing in the field across from our housing estate. Tag or hide and seek. I was enjoying myself. Then I heard my oldest sister

Lizzy calling my name.

'Mary, you have to come in now,' she was shouting.

When I arrived at our house, I heard my sister shouting at one of my brothers. She was angry.

Lizzy was fifteen, and Mammy used to make her take care of us when she had to go anywhere, like shopping or over to Nana's. This really annoyed Lizzy because she wanted to hang around outside with the teenagers in our street.

I walked into the sitting room, and straight away, I knew something was not right. I felt my wee body tense up.

'Where is Mammy?' I asked my sister.

'She has gone out,' she replied. 'And I have to mind you brats!'

'You mean Mammy has gone out with Daddy?' I quivered.

'Yes,' she retorted.

'Did Daddy have his car?' My daddy used to fix cars for people he knew, so he always had a car.

'Yes!' my sister yelled angrily at me.

I was shaking I was so afraid; of what, I don't know.

'Do your homework,' my sister ordered me.

'But Daddy is drunk.'

'I know that,' she said. 'Daddy is always drunk.'

None of the fears or anxieties I had felt before could compare to the absolute despair I felt right then. I was literally shaking like a leaf. I thought my wee heart was going to explode. I had an overwhelming sense of doom.

All I could think was, 'My mammy is gone. Will my mammy come back? What if she does not come home?' I started to cry. I could not help it. The tears just came. Suddenly I was screeching. 'I want Mammy home!'

My oldest sister was not going to put up with my nonsense. This was bad enough for her being taken in early to mind us kids.

'Quit your whingeing!' she roared at me. 'Mammy won't be long.'

I don't know how long my mammy was gone, but I was sitting up in bed trembling with fear and worry until I heard her voice as she came in the front door. Only then could I breathe normally again and sleep. Daddy did not come home with Mammy that night. Once a week, Daddy would come home drunk.

He and Mammy would fight, and he would be gone the next day. Some nights on his visits, he would bring us bottles of lemonade and crisps from the pub. We would all curl up on the sofa. Daddy played the harmonica. He would play tunes for us, and we would all sing along. I loved to sing. These rainbow moments were precious to me.

When we'd wake up the following morning, Daddy would be gone again. A short time later, the visits stopped altogether, but for me, this was only the beginning of a long, painful spell in my young life, where I spent every day consumed with worry and fear.

I started to cling to my mother with a force so strong. Everywhere she went, I begged her to take me with her. Over to my nana's, shopping, visiting her friends, I would cry and screech 'Please, can I go with you, Mammy?' I always had a fear that when Mammy went out, she wouldn't come back.

This became intolerable for my mother. I was behind her everywhere she went. It also caused war between my siblings and me.

'Why can't I go with you, Mammy?'

'Why does Mary get to go everywhere?'

I simply couldn't eat, sleep, or think straight when Mammy wasn't there. To add insult to injury, I had started to develop nervous twitches. Out of nowhere, I'd get an insatiable urge to blink my eyes and twitch my body constantly.

This reaction of nervous twitching progressed, and I began to pick at my clothes constantly. Even worse than that, I started to pick at my sisters' clothes as they lay beside me in bed at night. My poor sisters were tortured. Rows began between them.

'You lie beside her!'

'No, you lie beside her!'

'Mammy, will you tell Mary to stop picking us when we lie in bed? She keeps picking at us with her fingers. It's like sleeping with a bloody pigeon!'

I would promise not to do it again, but as soon as I lay in bed, this fear of the unknown would come upon me, and my picking would start again.

'Mary,' my mother would say. 'Will you, please, stop picking at your sisters in bed?' 'Why do you do that, child?'

I'd get angry then when Mammy would say this to me because I did not know why I was doing all these strange things. I was as baffled as everyone else in the family.

'I can't help it!' I would retort.

My mother knew then I was clearly very upset. 'It's okay, love. It's just a habit. You will grow out of it.'

That was that, but for me, as a ten-year-old child, I was so frightened. I did not understand what was happening to me. It left me frustrated. Most of the time, I could keep my twitches under control, but if I was worried or anxious about something they escalated.

My classmates had a field day mocking and giggling at me. The one occasion that is foremost in my mind was when us sixth class girls had to go to the church to practise for our Confirmation. We were going to be joined with the boys from sixth class. We had an all-girl primary school with the all-boys school adjacent to ours, and this would be the first time we would be mixed together.

Now, the rest of the girls in class were very excited about this event. I was a shrivelling mess at the thought of being in the company of the boys, which aggravated my twitches. Well, by the time I got to where I was instructed to sit in the chapel, fear consumed me, and the twitching began. By the time we were seated, I was twitching around in the pew, like a fish reeled in from a boat. I began to blink my eyes continuously.

Needless to say, for the girls and boys, this freak show was highly amusing. They all exploded with laughter. When our teachers told them to be quiet, they had to cover their mouths to hold in the giggles. Everyone pointed and stared at me, and I knew I was on display, yet I could not stop.

So went my first introduction to the opposite sex. I can say that the absolute humiliation and embarrassment I felt on that day is still vivid in my mind.

My mother stopped making any remarks to me about these strange quirks, although I would catch her sometimes staring at me, with a look of concern on her face. She obviously knew I was going through an unusual transition from childhood to adolescence, but she refrained from putting the spotlight on me.

Sometimes I would look around at my siblings, my friends, and classmates, and I would wonder in frustration what was wrong with me?

Every morning, I woke up with yet another nameless fear inside. This traumatic time in my life turned me into a very insecure, confused fearful young girl, my mother became very worried. She decided to take me to our GP.

Mammy went in to talk to the doctor while I waited outside. A few minutes later, I was ushered in. The doctor asked me questions about school.

Did I like it? Was anything bothering me? Was I happy?

It was all very strange to me, this line of questioning. I just nodded or shook my head 'yes' and 'no' as I found appropriate. After a short while, the doctor turned to my mother and said, 'She is very thin, Mrs Tuite. Does she eat much?'

'Yes,' my mother replied. 'Like a horse. Although lately, her appetite is not as good as it was.'

'I do eat!' I roared at the doctor.

They both stared at me.

My anger rose at the cheek of this doctor asking, 'Do I eat?'

'That's fine, Mary,' the doctor said. 'I'm sure you do.'

Clearly, I was developing a sensitive nature. Yet another huge kick to my confidence for the future.

Mammy and I called into my nana on the way home from the doctor. As I sat in nana's sitting room playing with her wee dog Chummy, I overheard Mammy talking to Nana in the kitchen.

'The doctor says Mary is suffering from delayed shock from the dog bites. She is clinging to me because her daddy left. She is afraid I will too.'

I moved away from the door. I didn't know how to process this information.

I heard it, and it only left me feeling more frustrated. The commenting and mocking at my twitching from my friends and siblings seemed to have eased off after that time, so ultimately, my nervous twitches also became less and less. I still suffered isolated attacks when faced with anything that frightened me.

My sweet mother must have called a meeting with all my nearest and dearest to make this happen.

In the meantime, the end of my years at primary school was drawing near. Sister Martina wasn't so bad, really. Oh yes, she was wicked, but she never frightened me, which is strange because nearly everything frightened me then.

One day, near the end of our term with her, she was late coming to class. Naturally, we girls made the most of this spell of freedom. We were giggling, chatting, making paper planes, and throwing them across the classroom at each other.

Sister Martina entered the classroom quietly.

'What is going on here? Disgraceful behaviour!' she bellowed. We were ordered to stand in line side by side at the top of the class.

Then the ruler came out. The funny thing is I had no fear of this at all. In fact, I was curious while I waited for my turn. One of the popular girls beside me started to cry before she even got her slap. I remember thinking what is wrong with her? Sure, it's only a wee slap. There is no way I'm going to cry!

I'd get plenty of dead arm thumps from my big brothers. Sure it can't be worse than them, and I was right. It was a quick sting, and then it was gone. Dead arm thumps were a lot worse.

On the last day of school, we all got our exam papers and drawings to take home with us. My results were poor as I had expected with shame. I was briefly looking through them when I heard Sister Martina call my name out from the top of the classroom. I looked up at her warily, afraid that she would make a remark about my poor results. Then she said a very curious thing.

'Mary,' she began. 'You, child, have the brains to take you to university.' She then paused and stared at me with a solemn look on her face. 'It's such a pity you are sitting on them.'

We stared at each other in silence for a moment. I was very confused.

All the girls were staring at me, but I had no response to this statement. The moment passed. All I was thinking then was, 'I don't want to go to university! I couldn't leave my mammy! And how on earth can you sit on your brain?' What a funny little nun, Sister Martina was! Oh yes, she knew me well.

I hated secondary school and, despite the fact that I was only twelve years old, my daily plea to my mother was, 'Please, Ma, can I leave school? I'll get a job I promise.' My poor mother was tortured by me.

'You're too young, Mary. Stay at school for another year and then we will see.'

'A year, Mam!' I bellowed.

My mother looked at me, sternly. 'Look, Mary, you have to stay in school, child, and that's an end to it. Now stop asking me this every day.' Ma gave me that I-mean-business-here stare, so I wisely stopped asking and trudged on miserably.

I don't have much to say about my time there. Tara and I went together to secondary and were still friends, but she had made a few new friends also, whereas I, on the other hand, stayed isolated much of the time. When we were in a crowd, I stayed quiet in the background, but Tara could chat and socialise easily. We were very different in that respect. I was self-conscious, sensitive, and my self-esteem was at an all-time low.

I had only done one full term and was a couple of months into the second when my mother finally relented and let me leave. I wanted new clothes. The girls at school all had lots of lovely clothes. I had none. To want to leave school so that you can have a job to get new clothes at the age of fourteen seems ridiculous, but that's how I felt then.

My clinginess to my mother had subsided by now. The humiliating twitching stage had left me too, although I was still a very insecure teenager.

Through all the years from my earliest memory in childhood up until the first day I started work, it was the rainbow moments that kept the fire burning inside me, those moments of joy, of laughter, and song;the family togetherness and the safety that I felt in our little home, surrounded by my loved ones. Most of all, the love and comfort I always felt. These were the things I bounced off. These rainbow moments kept the frightened little girl hidden away and strengthened my resolve to face the world.

Since I was only fourteen years old, I needed to forge the date on my birth certificate to get my job. You had to be fifteen to go to work in those days. This was nineteen eighty. My oldest brother changed my birth date using Tippex to cover up the original date. I don't think the production manager fell for it judging by his face when I handed it to him, but I got the job anyway, perhaps because my two older sisters were working there also.

It was a textile factory, and it was situated in the centre of town. This factory was to be my home from home for the next thirteen years of my life.

I met some of my lifelong friends here, gained many sewing skills, and extensive knowledge of working various sewing machines. I both hated it and loved it. Sometimes I felt that my life was going nowhere working from eight in the morning until five thirty in the evening five days a week, but I could never seem to find the motivation to get out, to better myself career-wise. Nor did I have the confidence. Fear of the unknown kept me grounded there.

Chapter 2

I was beginning to get many compliments and remarks around this time on my looks. People admired my long curly brown hair and blue eyes, or my long legs and slim figure. At the age of fifteen, I was turning into quite a swan, although I was still plagued with insecurities. It was nice to hear these compliments, but I never developed a big ego from them. In fact, it was quite the opposite. Hearing them made me blush. So just when I was finding my comfort zone again in life, yet another personality trait rose to the surface. Extreme shyness!

This was to the extent that if one of the boys from the cutting room just passed by me with a greeting of hello, my face would explode tomato red in seconds. This was excruciating for me, and it brought up all my worries, dreads, anxieties, and fears that I had hidden away since childhood. I started to get teased about it, which naturally made it even worse. So, no matter how pretty I was or how I looked to the outside world, it was no use to me because I was a trembling mess.

It got so bad for me that I became quite anti-social, especially around men. I had my few very close friends though who were understanding and did not tease me, but the world is a big place, and it's hard to hide from.

I remember one day feeling so frustrated about the kind of person I was becoming, that it brought up an anger in me, which I had never experienced before. Questions whirled around in my head. 'Why am I like this? What is wrong with me?'

There were no answers out there for me. I felt isolated inside, and self-pity consumed me. I simply had to talk to someone, but that in itself posed a problem. If I started talking to someone about my extreme shyness, the actual thought of expressing this would turn my face beetroot red. My heart would race, and I would start to sweat from every pore. I just couldn't.

In that era of the early 80s, in our small town, there was never a mention in my circles about talking to a psychologist or going to a counsellor at your school. We didn't have any of those services where we lived. Perhaps our family GP could have given my mother the number of a specialist for me to talk to if I'd wanted to do that. She never suggested it to me.

I think my mother knew me too well. She would have known the reaction I would have to being asked to go to a psychologist. She didn't want to put a spotlight on my personality quirks. From experience, she knew what my reaction would be. The one and only time she questioned my behaviour to my face, it had enraged me simply because I had no answer as to why I felt the way I felt. My mother saw how upset I got when she put any emphasis on my strange behaviour.

The truth is my anger was a spin-off reaction to my humiliation for being the way I was. Mammy knew that, therefore, she kept quiet in the hope that I would eventually grow past all my insecurities.

It was the same scenario with my friends too. I tried so hard not to let my shyness, my social awkwardness, come to the surface with my friends. It was extremely hard, until one day my friend Jane had a boyfriend problem and for some strange reason, she turned to me as her shoulder to cry on.

Now, I was the last girl in the world who could advise on boy trouble. I could hardly even talk to one without turning into a freak. Yet, to my amazement, these words of wisdom came falling from my lips as I held her, comforting her through her broken teenage heart. Afterwards, Jane turned to me as she wiped her tears and said, 'Thanks so much, Mary. You helped me a lot.'

All I recall saying was something like, 'Don't worry, Jane. You are young. There will be other boys. If he really cared for you, he would not have hurt you. You deserve better than him.' Obvious clichés like that. Jane, however, felt much better after pouring her heart out to me.

She was so grateful, and she told our other mutual friends how much I had helped her with her situation. Suddenly I became everyone's agony aunt. It took on a life of its own with absolutely no effort on my part.

So began my journey as the gang's comfort blanket and confidant.

In hindsight, this era of me being the shoulder to cry on was a saving grace for me. While I was being the helper to my friends, it also helped me. It prevented me from being able to focus on my flaws and fears, and it also brought a well-needed boost to my crumbling confidence. To see them being relieved by having a chat with me was extremely fulfilling. I always felt a serene calmness inside afterwards.

This was a refreshing break from my normal fear-filled anxious state. However, the fact that I had happily been given this role with my friends also meant that I could not contemplate speaking to them for relief from my shyness and emotionally fragile state. I liked being their mentor and, the truth was, I was too proud as well as extremely embarrassed.

My main objective was to keep my odd quirks hidden as much as possible from the outside world; they were so humiliating

However, on this nameless day, my mind was in turmoil. I felt like my brain was crushing my skull. I had to seek help. The ducking and diving to hide my shyness were taking its toll on me.

I realised right then that the only person in the whole world I could trust or feel comfortable with to talk to was my mother. I decided I would mention it to her later after work. In a quiet slot that evening in the sitting room, I began.

'Mam,' I said. 'There is something wrong with me.'

My mother looked up from her armchair by the fire, a very worried look on her face.

'What is it, love?' she asked warily.

'I blush an awful lot, and I get very shy and embarrassed when anyone teases me. It's very annoying, Ma,' I whinged.

My sweet mother looked at me then with relief on her face and a slight smile on her lips. 'Aw, Mary, love,' she said. 'You get that from me. I was always very shy when I was your age. I used to blush when I looked at myself in the mirror! Don't worry about it, love. You will grow out of it.'

I was flabbergasted at this. 'What? When will I grow out of it, Mam?' I roared. 'I want it gone now!'

'Soon, love. I promise,' my mother replied sympathetically.

'Well,' I thought. 'This is just great! I have inherited this burden...'

And so it was for me then, just another flaw in my character, which I had to try to adapt my life around. It was hard work. Isolating myself became necessary so that nobody got to know the real me, including myself.

The majority of the workforce in the factory were in their teens to early twenties. Some had boyfriends and husbands. I hung around with the free and single girls. They had no issues with me nor I with them. We accepted each other, warts and all, even though I hid most of mine to the best of my ability. Also we were all from a working-class background and had a lot in common. I could confide in them and them in me. It was precious.

A new roller disco opened in our town. I had a full year of work in the factory under my belt – I was almost sixteen then – and the girls and I were very anxious to try it out. It had been years since any of us had been on roller skates. A few of my friends and I decided to go on a Friday night. The queue from the entrance hatch went all the way along the street. We didn't mind waiting. We were all excited and chatted and giggled away to each other as we waited.

We finally got to the ticket hatch, and I could hear the DJ playing all the latest songs. We got settled in, laced up our boot skates, and away we went on the floor. Aw, it was a blast. We fell, we got up, and we fell again. It didn't take me long though to get my balance and skate easily around the floor without falling. 'This is what enjoyment means,' I thought.

The DJ then announced to everybody to clear the floor for the slow set. I said to one of the girls then, 'What is a slow set?'

'It's when a boy has to skate with a girl,' she replied.

'Oh,' I said and then for some reason I started to tense up even though there were no boys with us. I was afraid. I'd felt like a bird freed from a cage while I was skating around that hall. Now, I was sitting there, apprehensive and worried.

I was right to be. Just then one of the girls said, 'Look, those three boys are looking over at us. Maybe they are going to ask us to skate with them.' The girls seemed excited about this prospect.

I could not even respond to that. I was shaking. My heart was thumping like a drum in my chest. I thought about trying to leave or going to the ladies but to do that I would have to pass those boys, and that was not an option for me. Then my worst nightmare came true.

'Mary, look, that tall boy is looking at you...look...look, he is coming over.' My friend was giggling and nudging me incessantly.

I was frozen on the spot. I could not look up. I put my head as far down as I could without putting it between my legs. My friend kept on at me, with my head still down I growled at her, 'Shut up, will you?' I said it with such venom that my friend went quiet.

'Do you want to skate with me?' I lifted my head up slightly and looked at him for a split second.

'Go on, Mary.' the girls were nudging me. It was dark. He could not see my beetroot-red face or my shaking hands, and I admired him for having the courage to ask so, I said, 'Yes,' in a low, croaky voice. He put his hand out for mine, and I took it.

As we walked to the floor to skate, there was an explosion of laughter behind us. I turned to see all his friends were huddled together, pointing and laughing at us.

'Well, that's not a very nice thing to do to your mate,' I thought. 'Isn't he nervous enough without having his friends sneering at him?'

Just then, the boy I was with nudged me.

'I'm only joking with ya.' He giggled. 'Look at my feet.'

I looked down. He didn't have any skates on. I looked back up at his face, totally bewildered.

'Ha ha!' He laughed in my face and then ran off the floor back to his seat.

I tried to scramble as fast as I could with my skates on back to my seat with my head down in humiliation. I could still hear him and his friends laughing behind me.

I slumped in the chair and angrily announced, 'I'm going home.' As I began to unlace my boots, my friends realised how upset I was. They tried to cheer me up.

'Ah, come on, Mary. It was funny. Sure, it's only a bit of crack. Stay, don't let it spoil your night.'

I stared at them in reply. My look spoke a thousand words, and they knew it. I announced adamantly, 'I'm going home.' I got up, stormed past those boys with my head down in shame and embarrassment and left.

I have truly never forgotten how humiliated I felt that night; such was my sensitivity. Worse than that, though, was the anger and resentment that boiled inside me towards that boy. I hoped he would burn in hell forever. To my mind, he had turned my perfect night into my worst nightmare, and for that, there would be no forgiveness.

I suppose for an ordinary minded person, this episode is humorous, but for me, it was simply another crushing blow to my already crumbling confidence. I was just different, that's all.

'Are you coming to the skating Friday night?' one of my friends asked me while we were on our lunch break at work.

I did not want to say no. I was sure the girls would think I was afraid because of the incident last week which I was, but I couldn't let them know that, so I said, 'Yes, I'd love to.'

I made the decision then that I would not let that boy's behaviour stop me from enjoying skating; although along with that decision I also made a firm resolution to refuse any boy who asked me to skate with him.

We were in the ladies' toilets, fixing our hair, and my friend Jane turned to me.

'Mary,' she said. 'Guess what I have in my pocket?'

I looked at her curiously.

'What?' I replied.

She had a mischievous look on her face. 'Come on into the cubicle, and I'll show you.' When we locked the door, she reached into her pocket and took out a half bottle of vodka.

I stared at her wide-eyed. 'Wow!' I said. 'Where did you get that from?'

'My cousin,' she replied. 'He and his family were visiting yesterday, and I asked him to go to the off-licence and get it for me.'

I was speechless.

Jane was a couple of months younger than me, and we'd become friends straight away. She'd started in the factory a few months after me, and she was witty and carefree. Jane took out a can of orange from another pocket.

'I have a mixer too; do you want to share it with me?' she urged.

Suddenly I felt that familiar flutter in my chest, but this time, no fear followed.

'Okay,' I said with anticipation.

I was fixated on the bottle while Jane poured it slowly into the can of orange and began to swirl it around to mix them together.

'Do you want to take the first sip?'

'No,' I replied instantly. I wanted to see her reaction to the first swallow. I was glued to her face.

She took the can from her lips.

'Well?' I said. 'What is it like?'

She let out a long sigh. 'It's warm,' she croaked. 'I can feel the heat going down my throat.'

'Does it taste okay?' I asked. I felt the excitement building up in me.

'Yes,' she replied. 'Here, your turn.' She passed me the can.

My hands were shaking slightly as I took it from her. My friend was right. The first thing I felt was the heat going down my throat.

'What is it like for you?'

'It tastes a bit strong,' I said.

'Nah,' she replied, 'it's fine,' and the truth is it really was fine.

We drank the rest, sharing it gulp for gulp. We then put the can in the bin and went to the seating to put our skates on.

As I was lacing my boots, I felt strange. A sort of out of body sensation came over me, followed by a wonderful, calm, serene feeling, and I remember smiling. I lifted my head to look around and realised I was a little dizzy. I turned to my friend Jane.

'Do you feel a bit strange?'

'Yes,' she replied. 'A wee bit. It's great, isn't it?'

'Yes,' I said. 'It's fantastic!' And it was.

The most amazing part of that night was that the shy, fearful, anxious girl who'd walked into that hall earlier had disappeared. I was transformed into a smiling, chatty teenager, full of confidence. The person I'd always wanted to be and the promise that I'd made myself earlier in the week to never skate with a boy again, well, rubbish to that! I said yes to every boy who asked me and who were wearing skates.

It was the best night of my life. To think that a few gulps of alcohol could turn me into this amazing person.

I decided that night that this alcohol was the solution to all my problems. What a reassurance that was for me. It was euphoric. I would never again have to suffer from my crippling anxieties and fears or have to force myself to try to be like everyone else in a social setting. All I needed was alcohol, and I would use it. That was my firm resolution.

They say when something seems too good to be true, it usually is.

In my teenage years, from the age of sixteen to the age of twenty, I began to change again. It was a rebellious stage of life, and I excelled at it. I'd found the solution to my fears and insecurities in a bottle now. Therefore, with that knowledge, I could face social settings fearlessly. I gained the confidence I'd always admired in others.

Ultimately, I began to crave the nightlife, pub life, discos, and partying in friends' houses. I couldn't get enough.

So many times, my mother would ask me to 'Stay in tonight.' So many times I said, 'No, I'm going out.'

We had many rows. It went from my living on my mother's every word to totally ignoring her. I would stay out all night at weekends at friends' houses, with no compassion for how worried she was.

Sometimes, she would lock me out in an attempt to scare me into coming home early. It never worked though. I would come home drunk at all hours and throw stones up at my brother's window to wake him up to let me in. I was totally self-absorbed. My attitude was: it's my life, my choice. To put it simply, I just did not care.

Another new Mary was evolving, and I liked this one because she was not afraid. She was the life of the party, oozing confidence, funny, and carefree. Albeit I had my aid with me, my alcohol, but never mind.

My reasoning was that if getting drunk on the weekends took away the fear and tension of my inability to connect at work, and my constant worry about my extreme shyness, it was worth the rows with Mam. It was worth the hangovers. Nobody else's thoughts or feelings on the subject mattered to me. I refused to let even a niggling thought of guilt into my mind.

During my teenage years, I frequently saw my father while out socialising in bars. Sometimes he would be drinking in one of the bars I frequented with my sister Erin or my friends. The first of these chance meetings was in a small bar that was in walking distance from our home. My sister Erin and I were ordering our drinks when suddenly she nudged me. When I turned to face her, she was staring at someone sitting alone at a table in the corner across from the bar. I looked to where she was staring and froze.

'It's Dad,' Erin whispered into my ear.

'I see that,' I replied abruptly,

The bar was quite empty this particular Friday night, with just a few regulars on the bar stools. Our view of him was slightly angled so that we only saw the side of his face. He hadn't seen us yet, but there was no mistaking our dad. He had a great big head of curls and long locks that grew down the side of his face, almost touching his chin.

We stood for a moment simply observing him as he lifted his pint of Guinness and sipped away. My first reaction was to leave. I felt my hands beginning to shake.

Then Erin said, 'Will we go over to him?'

'I don't know, Erin,' I replied nervously. 'I don't think I can. I mean, what will we say to him?'

She shrugged in reply.

It was an awkward situation for both of us. The first person who came to my mind was my mother. What would she think of us if we sat with Dad?

Erin interrupted my thoughts. 'Sure, we can just say hello, Mary. What harm is that?'

I was afraid. My heart began to jump in my chest. Erin seemed calmer, but then none of my siblings seemed to suffer from the fears that constantly crippled me in life. Erin nudged me again.

'C'mon,' she said. 'We will only go over for a minute.'

Before I could decide, she was heading across the bar to where Dad was sitting. I took a big gulp of my beer before following her. I stopped halfway to observe Dad's reaction to seeing my sister.

As Erin approached him, he turned. With his eyes wide, he bellowed, 'Ahh, Erin, my girl,' and he immediately grabbed her in a big hug.

Witnessing, this frightened me even more. 'How will I react to that?' I thought. As I stood frozen to the spot, Dad looked past Erin and saw me,

'Ahh, me wee Mary. Come over!' he shouted across the bar room.

With my head down in embarrassment, I obeyed and went over to the table he was sitting at. I received the same greeting as my sister. He devoured me in a big hug, and it made me want to cry. Fighting that emotion, I sat at the table with him. My sister sat facing me. Dad pulled his chair in close to us and began asking us how we were.

'Fine,' I said coldly.

Dad stared at me momentarily then turned to Erin. I sat motionless as they chatted briefly. The first thing I became aware of was the fact that Dad was drunk, which was not a shock. I don't recall ever seeing Dad without a drink, although he obviously was some of the time at home, but I have no memory of those days.

Dad wasn't incoherent drunk just enough that it was noticeable. The next thought that came to my mind was, 'I bet he wouldn't greet us like that if he was sober.' I felt anger towards him then; instantly, guilt followed that.

As Erin and he chatted away, I couldn't stop thinking about my mother. I felt like I was betraying her somewhat by sitting here in Dad's company, knowing what we knew of his other woman and family. In my heart, I knew the resentment Mam held for Dad. He'd hurt her and her children badly.

Dad began asking me questions; trivial things like, was I working? Did I have a boyfriend? I simply sat rigid nodding or shaking my head in response. I was finding it hard to restrain this tearful emotion that was rising in me. I could tell by Erin's facial expressions that she also felt nervous and slightly uncomfortable although she was handling herself better than me. She could talk to Dad with relative ease.

There were no deep discussions. It was all very casual chitter chatter about our siblings and us. Dad was going down memory lane, talking about us when we were children. Different funny things we would do or say. I spent most of the time simply staring at his face.

Dad had big eyes, and they were an unusual colour of grey mixed with green. I had forgotten that until then when I saw him again.

I began trying to slot his face back into my memory as my father. This was a challenge as he spoke about the past. I simply had no memory of what he was talking about. As he laughed and joked away, I found myself suddenly wishing he was still in my life. I began to imagine what it would be like for us all to go home together as a family. Unfortunately, as I continued to observe rather than participate in this wee get together, my anger began to rise more.

'Surely, he wants to know how Mam is,' I thought. 'Why is he being so jolly and inconsiderate of her feelings when he knows how much he hurt her?' These thoughts began to impact on me physically, making my body tense up. My heart was palpitating wildly.

Suddenly, I got an overwhelming urge to get away from him. I did not have the courage to confront Dad about what he had done to all of us, and it was becoming more obvious that he was not going to open anything up about the past in that sense. The awareness that my dad seemingly simply had no respect for Mammy or us, to be acting so indifferent, hit me hard.

My illusions of him were smashed there and then. Clearly, Dad was never a father to us or husband to his wife in the conventional sense. I was aware of that. However, somewhere at the back of my mind, I'd always held on to the notion that he did care; that he loved Mam and us; that he would come to us to make his amends;

tell us he loved and missed us. He would say he was sorry, and he wanted to be part of our lives again. While I sat there and witnessed his trivial chatter, though, I realised this would never be.

My dreams were dissipating before my eyes. Our meeting was more like that which you would have with a long-lost cousin or friend. Perhaps this awakening was the reason for the overwhelming sadness that was devouring me. I could feel tears welling up in my eyes. I had to get away.

I quickly finished my drink.

'Erin, I have to go,' I announced as she was talking away to Dad about her boyfriend, Paul. She and Dad looked at me, surprised at my outburst.

I avoided both their stares as I got up from the chair to leave.

'Ah,' Dad said. 'Do you have to go, girls?'

'Yes,' I replied sharply. 'We do, Dad. I'm meeting my friends uptown. They are waiting for me.' I answered him, keeping my head lowered to avoid his stare. I was so afraid that I would cry. This sadness was beginning to overpower me, and I simply could not, under any circumstances, let him see my tears. I was too proud for that.

In addition, neither Erin nor my father seemed to be feeling emotional like this. I was different, that's all. It was embarrassing for me now.

Dad gave us another hug and kiss on the cheek.

I abruptly broke free from his arms and left the bar almost running out, with my sister coming behind. Outside, I regained my composure quickly. I knew I would be okay once I had left him.

'Are you okay?' Erin asked, concerned as we stood outside the bar.

'Yes,' I lied. 'I'm fine. I just felt awkward there, Erin, with Dad.'

'Yeah,' she replied. 'Me too, but it was good to have a wee chat with him though, wasn't it?' She looked at me in trepidation for my response. Erin was two years older than me. I was taller than her, and she was like my dad in looks; fair with a few of Dad's features. I was more like my mother, dark-haired and tall.

'Yes, it was, I suppose, Erin,' I answered. 'But he was drunk. I found it hard to talk to him.'

'I know,' she replied solemnly. 'Still, I'm glad I saw him. Who knows if we ever will again,' she said.

I felt my eyes welling up again, as we shared a moment of silence between us –both afraid of sharing our feelings.

We had been brought up with an unspoken rule not to discuss our dad. I don't know how this came about. It simply seemed to have always been there between the whole family. It was on par with having manners, for us as kids. For that reason, this encounter with Dad left us both in unknown territory emotionally. The void in our lives where our dad should have been had affected all of us differently.

Where Erin could chat openly with Dad and feel grateful for getting to spend time with him, I felt deflated, almost regretting having seen him at all. That's because I was happy with my fantasy of what he was, whereas she was more mature of the fact.

I was upset about this instinctive knowledge that had come upon me; that clarity of the kind of person Dad was coming across to me to be. I over thought the whole scenario, which is very much the kind of person I was and can still be.

My sister and I went our separate ways that night; she to meet her boyfriend and I to go uptown to meet my friends and get drunk. I was looking forward to that more than ever before. We didn't tell our mother about our encounter with Dad. We knew it would upset her. Perhaps my mother knew very well just how much my dad would have had to stray outside his comfort zone to be a father to us then. That being the case, she would also have been very aware of how much it would hurt us if we were to lose him again.

Over the week following my chance meeting with my dad, I was in a low mood. My mother noticed this as the week went on. I was quiet at home and very touchy when approached by any of my siblings.

'Mam, Mary's narky again,' one of my younger brothers would say. 'Mary, leave your brother alone, please. What is wrong with you this week?'

'Nothing,' I retorted. 'I'm just tired, that's all.'

At night in bed that week after meeting my father, I began to get momentary flashbacks of Dad when I was young. Visions that I had no memory of previous to meeting him. As I slept, I could see him in my mind's eye coming and going from our home in different scenarios. One memory was of driving up to our small garage at the back of the house and smashing into it before braking the car. We were in the back garden playing. I'm not sure who was with me in this memory.

Daddy then got out of the car with the steering wheel in his hand. He was laughing and cursing in a jolly mood as he entered the house. I could hear him telling Mammy, 'The brakes on that piece of junk are going. I had to hand brake it to stop it.' He was laughing heartily about this, while I and whoever was with me were left standing in the garden frozen to the spot in fear.

Remembering that incident shook me then. Another one that came to my mind, that week after our meeting, was of Daddy coming into our house with an odd-looking gun. I was very small because I was looking up far to get a glance of it in his hand as he stood in the doorway of our sitting room. In my memory, I heard him say to Mammy, 'It's a nail gun. Where're the boys?' He was shouting and jolly as usual. He was drunk.

I remembered looking at my mother's face. I saw fear in her eyes, which made me afraid also.

Daddy called my older brothers in from the street. He wanted to show them how to work the steel nail gun. The flashback I got after that was Mammy's voice as she was shouting at my father because he'd let my older brothers shoot nails into the walls in our sitting room.

These flashbacks left me in awe as I stared into space in bed at night that week. The images upset me interrupting my sleep, which in turn led to my agitated state over those days. I didn't want to remember these incidents or any other in which my father was involved, simply because they disrupted my mental state which were not very stable to begin with during these turbulent teenage years. I wanted to forget him again. I had no peace while he was in my thoughts and that sadness I had felt while in his company briefly, kept creeping up on me when he was on my mind.

Therefore, I made a firm resolution to put all visions or memories of him back into the filing cabinet at the back of my mind once and for all. I refused to let him disrupt my thinking any further. The weekend was upon me then. It was my time to go out, get drunk, and party. Nobody was going to ruin that for me, and especially not my father.

The rare times I saw my dad in a bar after that night, I avoided him.

I never stayed long enough for him to notice me. My friends understood when I'd say I had to leave. They respected my wishes without probing. Eventually, I stopped seeing him in any bars. I gave it no thought. The flashbacks stopped, and I got on with my life. My weekends were all that were important to me then.

Those few nights a week were precious to me. They were the hours in my life where I was completely happy, relaxed and, most of all, free from fear. Even though it was a false reality, clouded with alcohol, a pretence, or living a lie, it did not matter to me.

I often reflect while writing here on what my poor mother endured raising me, living through my ever-changing moods, and personality disorders. I'm certain my selfishness and lack of consideration, actions, and deeds left her with many a sleepless night, especially through my early teens. Plus, I'm only one of seven, and she had to spread herself around, with no help or support from my father. I'm deeply sorry for the worry I caused her, and although she asked for no apology, it's just and right that I offer it. Her unconditional love surpasses any I have ever known.

Our wee house was always a hive of activity, particularly at weekends.

'Will you hurry up in the bathroom,' was the most common request.

Sisters getting ready for dates, brothers getting ready to go out to the disco with mates, and my younger brothers fighting over the TV. It was bedlam, but I loved it.

My poor mother would be trying to bring calm to the storm to no avail. One Friday evening, it was the usual madness, except I was not going out that night. I was saving my meagre wages for my twenty-first birthday party, which was coming up in a few weeks.

My mother was planning a wee party at home for me. She was inviting my nana, my grand aunt Lily and some neighbours and friends.

'That's fine, Ma,' I said. 'But I want to have a pub party for all my friends.'

'Well,' she said. 'Mary, I can't afford to have two parties for you.'

'I know that, Ma,' I replied. 'I will pay for it.'

I was deep in thought that Friday evening at home, arranging what I wanted for my big night. A loud knock on the front door disturbed my concentration. I could hear my siblings running up and down the stairs.

'Ma, where's my razor? Ma, are there any towels?'

Nobody seemed to have heard the knocking at the front door except for me.

'I'll get it!' I shouted to nobody in particular.

I opened the door to my oldest brother's friend.

'Hi ya,' I said to him. 'I'll get him now for you. Ciaran!' I roared up the stairs. 'It's the head for you.'

Suddenly there was silence from upstairs. I ignored it and went back to the sitting room. I could hear my brother chatting at the door briefly and then closing it.

He then came charging into the sitting room over to me. I looked up at him, confused. 'What?' I said.

'Why did you call him the head?' he growled at me. 'He doesn't know I call him that nickname. His name is Denis! You embarrassed the shite out of me there. I couldn't look Denis in the face, yae ejet ya.'

'How was I supposed to know his real name?' I retorted. 'You always call him the head.'

'Mary, for God's sake,' my mam joined in the accusations.

'What, Ma? I didn't know that he didn't know!'

My brother marched out, grumbling under his breath. 'How am I going to face the head again?'

'Stop calling him that name!' my mother yelled after him.

My big night had arrived – my twenty-first birthday party. This was in December 1987. We had the little family one my ma wanted on my birthday date, which was a midweek night, and I had the pub party planned for the Friday night of that week.

I enjoyed my wee house party too. It was nice. I love my nana and my aunt Lily, especially when they had the few Baby Chams in them and the mocking and singing started. It was something to behold that's for sure.

But it was time for the big party now. My fear crept in and out. My main concern was my awkwardness around the boys from work because I had invited everyone from the factory. I really wanted to have confidence that night and be chatty. I was not too concerned, though, because now I had my solution, my alcohol. It never let me down, and that night I was getting drinks bought for me too, for my birthday, so I didn't need much money to buy drinks. Our factory wages were poor even for that era.

The night was going great. I was loving my life right then. All my family and friends were there. The DJ was playing all my favourites, and we were all singing along. Then I saw a couple of the boys from the factory coming through the door.

I was okay though because I was intoxicated; not fall-down drunk, just a bit tipsy. My body and brain had always had an enormous capacity for alcohol then, or as my friends would say, 'You can drink any man under the table, Mary.'

To think I used to be proud of that.

So, I was just drunk enough to be brave. One of the new boys in our factory came up to me then, to wish me a happy birthday.

'Thank you,' I said. 'Would you like to dance with me?' I blurted out to him.

'Okay.' He was looking at me funny, sort of stunned. We danced and afterwards he said words to me that sobered me up in an instant.

'Mary,' he said, 'You never even lift your head to say hello to me at work. I thought you were a snob or something. All the boys do. How come that is? And you're all fun and chat with me now.'

I stared at him squarely in the eye. I could see by his expression that he wanted an explanation, but what was I to say to him?

'Eh, Peter, it's like this: when you say hello at work, my face explodes beetroot red and sweat starts to pour out of me. I'm extremely shy and socially awkward, so I have to avoid you and all men.'

That explanation was clearly not an option. What a freak I was! Instead, I said, 'I'm not a snob at all. Sometimes, I'll just be in a bad mood, that's all. I'm sorry for being ignorant. I don't mean to.'

'Okay,' he replied. 'So, will you talk to me at work next week?'

'Of course,' I lied. God help me on Monday.

I awoke to start my working week with dread. I felt like I was holding my breath the whole day. I didn't see him on Monday. I did see him on Tuesday. He was passing me by in the canteen. My heart started to race violently in an instant I was crippled with anxiety.

He stopped beside me. 'Thanks for inviting me to your party, Mary. Great night,' he said cheerily.

I kept my head down as he spoke. I just could not look him in the eye. *'Oh, please, go away, please,'* I silently begged him. I could feel my face flaring. I had to give him a reply. The word snob resounded in my head. I never wanted to be known as a snob. I mumbled under my breath, 'You're welcome,' without even looking at him. Then I raced past him and out the canteen door, cursing myself.

'What must he think of me?' I felt like the worst bitch on earth, and I knew I wasn't at all. But when that extreme shyness I suffered with took over, I had no control. Oh, why do I have to be this way? My mother told me a long time ago that I would grow out of this. When, Ma? When?

So it was for me then, for the majority of those teenage years, those factory years, I was basically an actress. Pretending to be someone I was not. Ducking and diving from encounters with people, especially boys, which would bring out this horrendous shyness and embarrassment.

I acquired a flair for avoiding certain people. The timing of everything in my day became crucial: queuing in the canteen, or at the clock machine because I would be expected to chat or join in a conversation. For me, that scenario was my worst nightmare.

In short, those young years in life where you should be thinking about what you want to achieve in the future – reaching for your goals and desires – enjoying the carefree life of youth. Laughing and having fun were, for me completely over-shadowed by a big dark cloud called fear.

I was an attractive young woman, tall and thin, and although I was aware that I was attractive, I just did not have the confidence to shine from within. Most of the time, I was moody and discontented. My siblings would mock me and call me narky, which I was. On the upside, I was not as socially awkward as I used to be. My shyness was still a major handicap in many situations but was not a daily battle for me anymore. It has left its scars on the inside.

When I was twenty-three, my youngest brother Ciaran and I were the last of the brood at home. All the others had flown the nest and had husbands, wives, and children. My youngest brother was in a relationship also.

I, on the other hand, was free and single and lived for the weekends and the pub life; partying with my friends and, of course, drinking. I worked my five-day week and spent all my wages on the nightlife and booze. Many of these nights were a blur to me. Once I got to a certain stage of drunkenness, I would have no recollection of it the next day. My friends would have to fill me in on how the night ended up and who I had been with. I was never a social drinker. It was all or nothing for me.

I used to mock friends who would sip at a small glass of beer for an hour. That wasn't drinking to my mind. Why bother drinking if you're not going to get drunk? Sure, isn't that what it's for? This was always my mindset because I used alcohol to get out of my own head. I thought everyone used it for the same thing…didn't they?

My only real hobby was reading. I loved a good novel. I read every night in bed. It's also a great way to escape from your thoughts, and it relaxed me. Nearly all the girls I knew and some of my friends had children and husbands. I thought they were barmy. It was the last thing I wanted. Although I loved my nieces and nephews, it was not for me. It was boring and mundane, as far as I was concerned. It was excitement I wanted. The more, the better, always yearning for something.

I would be asked out at the discos, agree to another date, and then I wouldn't turn up. Or I would give a fella my address to call on me the following week; then in my sobriety, I would be cringing at the thought of him calling to my home because I could not face him sober. I was a Jackal and Hyde character. In my drunken stupor, it seemed a brilliant idea to make a date for the following week.

My poor mother was tormented. Every Friday or Saturday night, it was the same cry from me. 'Ma, if any fella calls for me, tell him I'm not here. Please, Ma,' I would beg her.

'Aw, Mary, how many times are you going to make me lie to these poor fellas at the door for you? This is not right! Why do you make dates with them to call if you don't want to go out with them again?'

'I'm sorry, Ma. I won't do it again,' I'd lie. How could I ever explain to my ma that I would be so drunk, that I could not be sensible, or that a lot of the time I wouldn't even remember making a date until my friends reminded me the next day. Or even worse, I couldn't even remember what he looked like.

The truth is, in sobriety, I could not even look at a fella in a disco without getting embarrassed, never mind kiss one or dance with one. This was the cross I had to carry through all those years. It was how I was. I had no power over it. I stopped questioning. It was part of who I was, and I had to accept that, but never mind, I had alcohol now to mask it.

This twenty-third year of my life was a quiet time for me with my friends all settled into married life. The disco nights were fewer and fewer. I was still working at the factory. The talk was more and more about babies and sleepless nights and less about plans for the weekend.

Sometimes, I would wonder what it was like to be in a serious relationship; to share your daily life with a man, go shopping, watch movies, etc. For some reason, I just could not see myself in that scenario. In this being in love stuff. Well, perhaps, someday who knew?

Not that there was any man waiting in the wing patiently for me to say, 'Okay, love. Let's go make babies.'

But the very fact that I was thinking these thoughts made me realise that this was part of life, and that maybe I was changing. Maybe I was ready to grow up at last.

Our local pub was certainly not the Ritz! It had no grandeur, but it was cosy and clean and in walking distance from our home. So, that was good enough for me. Me, my brothers, their girlfriends, and a couple of my friends spent a lot of time there at the weekends. There was always a bit of crack. We played pool and put the jukebox on. I was quite good at pool, the result of being a pub goer from a ripe young age.

Sunday night was band night. I loved a live band. I could sit all night listening to the melodies of a good band. My youngest brothers played there regularly – one on drums and the other on bass guitar. There were quite a variety of musicians, who all gathered together and had what is known in the music scene as a jamming session. They would strut their stuff on a Sunday night.

On one of those particular Sunday nights, I noticed there was a new guy on stage with the usual bunch. He was singing and playing guitar. He had nice eyes and a great smile.

'Who's that fella?' I asked one of the boys.

'That's Dessie. He is Brian's mate. He jams with them sometimes.'

I looked up then into the face of my future husband. He smiled back.

Chapter 3

We got married on the eighteenth of September 1993. I was twenty-six, and my husband was thirty. That same year, the textile factory closed its doors. Ironically, it seems that this was one chapter of my life over, and a new one about to begin.

I was sad, afraid even. There was so much of me at those machines. In a lot of ways, the factory was my cocoon. I had found so many cherished friends there, and we'd shared many, many wild times together. It really was my home from home. In hindsight, I believe working there during my fledgeling years of insecurity and fear, shielded me from an outside world that I did not have the coping skills or the confidence to face. It was my safety net from life.

I was quite content to be unemployed for a while. This was the first time in thirteen years that I did not have to rise to face a working day. My husband and I had taken out a mortgage on our new home, so I had plenty of decorating and furnishing to keep me occupied.

Leaving my birth home was hard for me, though, for the first few months. I missed my ma terribly. She only lived two miles away, and I saw her nearly every day, but it wasn't the same.

From that very young age, I still held on to this fearful need to be with my mother. I even felt pangs of guilt for leaving her. My mother was like a soul mate to me. She was and always will be my comfort blanket. In truth, she was the only person in the world who really knew me inside and out.

That aside, I was very happy. Even better than that, I was content for the first time in my life, and I now know why.

For all those early years from my first memory of childhood to adolescence, I had become the great pretender, putting up a front to fit in. I'd be living with a knot of anxiety inside because I never knew what or who I would have to face on any given day. Knowing the character and insecurities I suffered with, constantly trying to hide for fear of being ridiculed or mocked. I worked so hard at not letting people see the real me; the shy awkward anti-social scared Mary, but now none of that mattered anymore.

My husband loved me warts and all. We had and still do have a good relationship. He is easy going and well-grounded. Quite unlike me back then, he was content in everyday life, enjoying the simple things. These qualities he possesses helped me just to be me. At last, I could relax and exhale all those fear-filled years away – no more pretending. The enlightenment I felt from that knowledge was beyond words –a true rainbow moment.

***

'Mary love, will you put more coal on that fire?'

My sweet nana was sitting up in her bed in the nursing home, staring at a blank spot on the wall facing her; bless her heart.

She was ninety-two years old and suffering from dementia. I had been married a few months then, and our new home was within walking distance to the nursing home. I played along with my nana's request so as not to confuse her more.

'Nana, it's very late. Best not to put more coal on at this time of night. Sure, it's warm in the room anyway.'

Suddenly, my Nana stared at me with a look of confusion. 'What do you mean, child? Sure, there's no fire in this place!'

Her behaviour was both humorous and sad, especially for my mother. Sometimes, my nana wouldn't even know my mother's name. The hardest thing my mother ever had to do was sign my nana into a nursing home. I felt pity for her. I realised that my mother also shared that bond, that closeness with her mother. But my nana was a liability to herself living at home alone. My mother did what was best for her mother's welfare and safety. She had no choice!

'You're some liar!' I yelled at my oldest sister Lizzy. 'You told me labour pains are not so bad!'

My sisters were walking up and down the corridors of the maternity wing in the hospital. I was in the early stages of labour with my first child. It was 14 October 1994. My husband was fidgeting, getting up, and then sitting down.

'I said that to you so that you wouldn't be afraid,' my sister replied. 'Anyway, I didn't think it was that bad.'

'Well,' my other sister Erin piped up. 'You must be made of rubber then. Of course, it's painful, Mary,' she comforted me. 'But it is worth it when you get to hold your baby in your arms.'

She was right. I gave birth to my son on 15 October 1994. He came into the world weighing eight pounds and four ounces, and he was beautiful. It was pure love at first sight. I didn't know I could ever possess such a perfect emotion. Nothing in the world could ever bring more joy than that which overwhelmed me when I saw his face. That rainbow moment topped all others and this one I would carry with me every moment of every day. I had never been happier.

As my husband and I settled contentedly into parenthood, we shared the responsibilities of our son's needs; night feeds, bath time, and nappy changing, which thankfully was not such a daunting task for Dessie. He was overjoyed at being a father. His devotion to his son was apparent.

Ryan had a big appetite, and it was a struggle to keep his feeding times spaced to every four hours. He greedily drank every ounce, but he was a very contented baby, sleeping the night through after a few weeks home.

When he was about four weeks old, I was sitting in the armchair with him on my lap; he had just finished his bottle. I was rubbing his back to relieve him of wind when suddenly I felt his rib cage contract, and he began to vomit violently. That, in itself, was not too alarming, but as I held him forward to vomit, I noticed with shock the volume of his vomit. It looked as though he had thrown up the whole bottle. What shocked me, even more, was the pattern of his vomiting. It shot from his mouth with such urgency across the floor.

I was stunned.

The episode lasted only a minute, and my baby was fine afterwards, but for some reason, I tensed up; an alarm bell went off in my mind. I had never seen a baby of four weeks vomiting so violently and at such a huge volume. I had plenty of experience with babies and feedings as all my sisters had children, and I had helped them on many occasions with theirs.

I changed Ryan's clothes and washed him down, then put him in his crib where he fell asleep peacefully. As I began the task of wiping up the vomit, I again felt ill at ease. I tried to push the foreboding feeling aside and reasoned with myself that all babies vomit.

Nevertheless, I mentioned it to my husband Dessie when he arrived home from work that evening. I just wanted to get it off my mind. He did not seem too alarmed. Like me, he felt it was normal for babies to vomit. He could tell by my agitation when I spoke that I was clearly worried, though, so he suggested that if it happens more often, we should take Ryan to our GP.

I agreed and put the episode behind me, forcing myself not to over think or dramatise it, which was one of my many characteristic behaviours.

Ryan held down the rest of his bottle-feeds for that day and night, yet I slept restlessly nonetheless. I found myself having the need to check on him regularly, as he slept in his crib beside our bed. At 7.30 the next morning, I gave Ryan his first feed of the day, which he hungrily devoured. It stayed down also, and I was relieved and happy to forget about the incident then.

Later in the afternoon, however, when he had his feed again, I felt his rib cage contracting. I knew instinctively what was coming, so I held him forward frozen in fear. My baby again began to vomit with the same urgency, and as before the floor area we were sitting at was covered in milk. Yet again, Ryan was fine afterwards. I was not. My mind kept telling me that this was not normal; something was wrong with Ryan. I had an overpowering instinct that all was not right with my baby.

I went through the same procedure of cleaning Ryan up and wiping up the vomit, all the while feeling more and more frightened of something I had no knowledge of. I phoned my husband.

'I'm worried,' I said, almost whimpering.

'Okay, Mary, just calm down.' Dessie could tell by my voice how anxious I was becoming. 'See if you can get an appointment with the doctor and,' he said. 'I can get time off work to go with you.'

'No,' I replied agitated. 'I can take him myself. You don't need to leave work.'

'You sure?' he questioned.

'Yes, it's fine,' I replied.

I phoned our doctor's surgery and got an appointment for the following morning at ten. I then phoned my mother to tell her about Ryan's vomiting, hoping she would have some words of wisdom for me to alleviate my foreboding worry.

She, like my husband, seemed nonchalant about it all even though I had explained the magnitude of vomit and how it shot across the room from his mouth.

'Do you not think that's a bit strange, Ma?'

She was quiet for a moment on the line. I could tell she was trying to pick the right words so as not to upset me any more than I obviously sounded while telling her.

'Look, love,' my mam said then. 'Try not to worry. I'm sure he is fine. But, then again, I haven't seen him vomiting, so it's easy for me to say. Your doctor will put your mind at rest when she examines him.'

'Yeah, I said,' in reply, nodding at the phone. 'I'll call tomorrow anyway to collect you.'

'Okay, love. Phone me if you need me in the meantime.'

I thanked my mother and hung up.

Mam and I regularly made dates to go into town, look around the shops, and then I'd take her to my home for her tea, or sometimes I'd have my tea in her house. We had planned this treat for tomorrow. I was looking forward to spending time with my mother. She was the only person in whose company I felt completely at ease.

I phoned my sisters that night also. After I explained about Ryan's vomiting, they too felt I was worrying unnecessarily. So it seemed I was a lone wolf with my concerns and foreboding thoughts, which emphasised to me that I was being overly dramatic about my baby's vomiting.

As I sat in the doctor's office with Ryan the next morning, I was beginning to think that indeed I was over thinking his vomiting. He had slept the night through and had kept his morning feed down also.

Our GP was checking his vitals and pressing gently on his abdomen as Ryan lay on the surgery bed. He was wriggling and wide-eyed as he looked around him.

After the examination, my doctor said that he seemed fine. 'He is a big healthy boy, Mary. I understand your concerns about his projectile vomiting, though.'

'Oh,' I said relieved. 'So, some babies do vomit like that then, Doctor?'

'Yes,' she said. 'It is common. You say it's only a couple of feeds he vomits?'

'Yes,' I said. 'Mainly afternoon feeds so far, Doctor.'

'Have you increased his ounces?'

I blushed slightly then. 'Actually, yes,' I replied. 'He is so hungry, and five ounces doesn't seem to fill him. He is still sucking away at the empty bottle, so I put him up to six.'

'That's fine,' she assured me. 'I don't know by looking at him what may be causing his vomits. Perhaps his digestive system is just adjusting to the extra food. Put him back on the five ounces for now and stick to his feeding time schedule as best you can. See if that alleviates his vomiting. If he still continues to vomit, then bring him up to the hospital. They may need to scan his stomach to see if there is an obstruction. I will give you a letter explaining his symptoms.'

'Okay. Thanks, Doctor,' I said solemnly.

'Don't worry,' she said to me, smiling. 'You're a first-time mother. It's natural to be over cautious, but I'm sure he is fine.'

I nodded, gathered my baby up, and strapped him into his baby car seat. I thanked her and left. While driving down to my mother's home, I began to feel frustrated.

Everybody around me was telling me not to worry and, ironically, the more I heard it, the more I worried. I simply wanted an answer to what was ailing my child and not a cliché.

I sighed out a long breath and shook myself, putting the negative thoughts out of my mind. I picked my mother up and filled her in on what the doctor had said.

My mother nodded and said, 'We'll see how he goes today before we worry anymore.'

I sighed. There was that word again. I hadn't had time to give Ryan his mid-morning bottle, so we went to my house to feed him before we went to town. Mam put the kettle on while I prepared a bottle for Ryan. I put an ounce less in the bottle as suggested by our doctor. We sat down and chatted while I fed my baby. My mother offered to help Ryan with his wind when he had finished his bottle. I believe she sensed my tension and fear.

I passed him to her and went to make a coffee.

As I stood at the sink, I suddenly heard a loud, deep burping sound. When I turned around, Ryan was once again vomiting violently except, this time, he was vomiting up what looked like scrambled eggs.

I dropped my cup in the sink and went to my child. I was frantic with shock. I took my baby from my mother's arms, and as I did so, he began to choke on the curdled milk chunks that were trying to escape from his stomach.

'Mam!' I screamed. 'What will we do?'

'Rub his back, Mary! I'll put my finger in his mouth to help him get the vomit out. Keep him faced down.' My mother began to scoop the chunks of curdled milk out of Ryan's mouth as he wretched.

I rubbed his back while I whimpered like a baby myself. Within a couple of minutes, the vomiting subsided, and my baby was fine but pale from the exertion of it.

I took him into my arms and rocked him gently, moaning in shock as I did so. I looked to Mam and she and I both turned to look at the mess on the floor. We stared at each other for a moment, both bewildered at what we saw in front of us. I noticed my mother was pale, obviously shocked as well.

I sat beside her. 'Mam, what is that?' I asked, looking at the vomit. Strewn through the curdled milk on the floor were what looked like tiny speckles of dried blood.

My mother looked closely. 'It looks like blood, Mags.'

That's my mother's pet name for me.

'What is going on, Mam?'

My mother put her arm around me as Ryan nestled on my lap. 'I don't know, love, what that is but I can tell you that I have never seen anything like that coming up from a four-week-old baby's stomach.'

Mam stared at me eye to eye then. 'You were right, love. That is definitely not normal.'

I rested my head on my mother's shoulder, and we sat like that for a few minutes trying to compose ourselves again.

'So glad you were here with me, Mam.'

'Me too, Mags. Now I think we better get this wee man to the hospital.'

I nodded.

I changed and washed my baby, and then my mother put him in his crib while I went to phone my husband. After telling him what had just happened, he too was shocked and told me he would get cover and be home in fifteen minutes.

Mam and I cleaned up the mess on the kitchen floor. As we were doing so, my mother wisely said, 'Mags, go and get a sealed container to put some of this into. We need to show it to the doctor.'

I nodded in agreement.

She looked at me square in the eye as we crouched on the floor with kitchen paper to wiped up.

'Your hands are shaking, Mary, love. Are you alright?'

I began to whimper. 'No, Mam, not really. I'm worried about my baby.'

'Of course, you are, Mags, and you've a right to be. I'll come with you to the hospital.'

I looked at my mother's sympathetic expression with gratitude for her being there with me. 'Thanks, Mam,' I said. 'What would I do without you?'

We sat in a cubicle in the accident and emergency department in the hospital an hour later. Ryan was sleeping in my husband Dessie's arms. He was stroking Ryan's face gently, silent in his concerns and worry for his son. I had handed in the letter my doctor had given me that morning.

It was a cold November day, and I could hear the wind whistling loudly in the trees outside. The sound seemed intensified and daunting as we sat silently huddled together in the small cubicle.

A doctor appeared within fifteen minutes and introduced himself. We greeted him, and he immediately asked my husband to lay Ryan down on the trolley bed so as to check him over. Dessie gently put Ryan on the bed, and the doctor began to ask us questions about Ryan's vomiting patterns. After explaining, the doctor opened up our baby's clothing and began to feel around his stomach area gently.

'His vomit is projectile, is that right, Mammy?' He looked at me.

'Yes,' I said.

Suddenly my mother interrupted. 'Mary, show the doctor the vomit you brought with you,' she urged me from the chair she was sitting in.

'Oh, yes, I forgot I had some. Here, Doctor,' I said as I reached into the plastic bag, I had brought the container in.

'Well, well, good thinking to bring that with you, Mammy,' he said, praising me,

'Actually,' I said humbly. 'It was my mother's idea.' I motioned him to where my mother sat in the corner of the wee cubicle.

'Aw.' He nodded to my mother in appreciation.

Mam smiled wryly, slightly embarrassed with the attention.

The doctor opened the container. He looked almost amused at the contents. 'Yes, well,' he sighed. 'Looks like there is bile in that also, which would be coming from the lining of your baby's stomach. '

'Doctor,' my husband said. 'What do you think is causing my son's vomiting?'

The doctor sighed again before answering, 'I'm not sure, and they only way we will find out is to admit your baby and do some tests for elimination purposes, and a scan on his tummy also.' He stopped talking then and looked at our baby boy who was contentedly lying there wide-eyed and fidgety. 'He is a very alert, big, healthy boy,' he said as he tickled Ryan's tummy. 'So, we want to keep him that way. Don't we, Mammy and Daddy?'

The doctor spoke to us like we were infants also, in an attempt to keep the situation light-hearted, which helped us to relax more.

'That's it then,' he continued. 'The nurse will organise a bed for Ryan, and you can take him to the children's ward. We will analyse this vomiting pattern, and try not to worry, Mammy,' he said, catching me off guard as he looked at me.

I was fixated on my baby's beautiful face as I sat with him on the trolley bed. My expression was telling tales as to how I felt; worry, dread, and pity. The word 'tests' told me that blood would be taken from my baby and who knows what other pain and discomfort he might have to endure. The very image of my baby being hurt filled me with anguish, yet I had no control over the situation.

It was the cruel-to-be-kind scenario. The only thing that helped me sustain my composure was the fact that Ryan was too young to be crying for us or wanting to go home.

Early that afternoon, Ryan was settled into his cot bed in a tiny cubicle in the baby ward. The nurse had told us that only the parents were allowed into the ward for protection from infections being carried in to the babies. My husband Dessie took my mother home. I hugged her and thanked her for being there for us and assured her that as soon as we knew what was going on with Ryan, I would let her know.

I sat down in the tiny cubicle with my son on my lap and began to feed him his bottle. Dessie sat beside me. I was tense and fearful of what may occur afterwards, although I was somewhat relieved that we were in the hospital with a nurse nearby if Ryan got into difficulty. The nurse came in when she saw that Ryan was feeding.

'Call me if he begins to vomit,' she urged.

The nurses were stationed just a few feet across the hall from Ryan's cubicle.

I nodded in reply.

Almost as soon as I'd sat my baby upright to relieve his wind, I felt the familiar contracting of his rib cage. I knew instinctively he was about to vomit.

'Call the nurse, Dessie!' I screeched. Seconds later, the vomiting began. The chunks of curdled milk spewed from our baby's mouth.

In an instant, the nurse took Ryan from my arms and along with another nurse they took over. One held our baby forward while the other helped him to cough up the chunks by rubbing his back in an upward motion.

I momentarily looked at Dessie. He had turned ashen white with shock at what he was witnessing his baby boy going through. I rubbed his back. 'It will stop soon, Dessie,' I whispered. 'Ryan will be fine.' I was relieved my husband was sitting down. I feared he would faint at the sight.

As before, the vomiting subsided within a minute or two and Ryan was fine afterwards.

Dessie got up from his chair and took Ryan from their arms, hugging him, and checking him over.

'He is okay,' one of the nurses said to my husband.

He sat beside me with our baby in his lap. He was shaking. I took Ryan from him and lay him in the cot to change and wash him while the nurses began to clean up the floor.

'We will report this episode to the doctor,' one nurse said. 'The poor wee fella. That's an enormous amount of vomit for a little thing like him.'

I nodded tearfully.

Dessie stood by the cot, holding Ryan's hand. 'That's not right,' was all he could say then, still shocked by the episode. An hour or so later, the doctor who admitted Ryan came to see us. He pulled a chair up directly in front of Dessie and me, where we sat against the wall in the tiny cubicle.

'The nurse has informed me about your baby's vomiting episode earlier,' he said in a calm, quiet voice. 'We feel this kind of vomiting is putting a lot of stress on your baby's stomach. For that reason, I'm going to ask you not to give him any more food until we get to the bottom of this.'

Dessie and I looked to our baby in unison as he slept in his cot, then turned our attention back to the doctor as he continued explaining.

'There is no point in making the wee man endure that discomfort.

We are going to get started straight away on him.'

My husband sat in silence as the doctor spoke. He sat back in his chair as he continued outlining the plans for Ryan.

'The first thing we will do is a blood test. After that, we want to do a lumbar puncture on Ryan.'

I sucked in a screech when the doctor said these words. With eyes wide in terror, I said, 'You don't think something is wrong in his brain, Doctor, do you?' I said in a whimper.

I felt my husband's hand grasping mine.

The doctor shook his head from side to side as he said, 'No, no, we don't believe so, but we want to eliminate any indication of a virus before we scan him.'

'A lumbar puncture is taking fluid from the spine, Doctor.'

'Yes, that's right,' he replied.

'It's a very painful procedure, I believe.' I was not sure how I had obtained that information, but I obviously had heard it from someone at one time in my life.

The doctor sighed again before answering, 'It is painful, but it's over quickly.'

'Is it really necessary, Doctor?' my husband asked. His voice was wavering.

'We feel it is, yes. As I said, it's a process of elimination.'

Dessie and I looked at each other, helplessly. What answer could we give? We knew we had to go with the doctor's advice. We nodded our approval to him.

'Okay,' he continued. 'After the lumbar puncture, we will scan your baby's tummy and, hopefully, by the end of this day, we will have an idea of what's going on. We will put an intravenous drip in also to keep him hydrated, but that won't be done until after we have done the scan and the lumbar puncture.'

The words 'lumbar puncture' tore at my heart. The very thought of my tiny son enduring such pain sent shivers down my spine. As if reading my thoughts, the doctor turned back as he was leaving and said, 'I advise you both not to hang around here while the lumbar puncture is being done. Best if you go to the café downstairs. It will only take a half hour or so to perform the procedure.'

We again simply nodded to him in response. What was there to say?

'The nurse will be in soon to take your baby for the procedure.'

We thanked the doctor, and he left. We had nothing to say to each other, Dessie and I. I didn't want to discuss what our baby would be enduring and nor did he. We both just stood by our son's cot and looked at him with love and pity; holding his tiny hand as he slept peacefully.

Fifteen minutes later, the nurse on duty in the baby ward came in to take Ryan down to have the lumbar puncture done.

We kissed our baby boy gently on the forehead as the nurse bundled him into her arms, awakening him from his slumber. He twitched and stretched his little body.

I walked out abruptly. I felt the tears welling in my eyes. Dessie came behind me. As we left, the nurse told us we could come back in a half hour or so.

At six o'clock that evening, Dessie and I sat in the hospital café with a coffee and a scone. I had only realised while putting the butter on my scone that it would be the first thing I'd had to eat since very early morning. Yet I had no real appetite.

Dessie went to the magazine rack when we had finished our scones and came back to the table with a magazine for me and a newspaper for himself. Thanking him, I began flicking through the pages. I found that I could not concentrate on reading. I closed it and looked up at Dessie. I saw that he too was flicking rapidly through the newspaper obviously struggling to grasp any story either. He went to the sports section.

I sat back and began to look around me half in a daze. Our table was beside the window of the café. An ambulance passing by caught my attention. As it passed by, I turned my attention to the comings and goings in the hospital café.

It was bustling all the time with both staff and visitors. At some tables, doctors and nurses sat chatting and laughing over coffees. Their pristine white coats and stethoscopes hanging around their necks brought the vision of my baby boy having a needle put into his spine. I shook my head and averted my gaze to a young girl with a man I assumed was her daddy, standing in front of the gift stand near the entrance to the café.

The little girl was about six or seven, I guessed.

'Daddy, can I buy Mammy a balloon?' she screeched, pointing to a purple love-heart-shaped balloon on a stick.

Her father was deciding which chocolates to buy; picking one box and another. 'Is it for your mammy or yourself that you want that balloon, Saoirse?' he said, smiling down at his daughter.

The little girl folded her arms in front of her in annoyance at her daddy questioning her motives. 'No, Daddy, it's not for me,' she retorted. 'It's a love heart for Mammy because I love her. '

Looking down at his daughter lovingly with sadness on his face, her father said, 'Okay, Saoirse, you can buy the balloon for Mammy.' The man ruffled the little girl's hair, and they shared a moment of silence as they looked at each other.

Witnessing this show of love and devotion brought a lump to my throat. I sighed and turned to look out the window once more.

My husband lifted his face from his paper then. 'Are you okay, Mary?' he inquired.

'Yes, I'm fine,' I lied.

He put his head back down to read the sports section.

I found myself looking around me once more at the constant stream of people in and out of the hospital café; some with arms heavy with gifts and cards for sick loved ones. I became aware of how insignificant the outside world with its stresses and responsibilities really was when faced with ill health, while in here, the outside world simply did not exist. You gain perspective.

Dessie and I arrived back to the baby ward after being gone for about twenty-four minutes. Ryan was back in his cot, awake and whingeing. I knew he was due his feed. My heart sank. 'How could I bear to listen to my baby cry with hunger?' I thought.

We went to his cot, and Dessie lifted him to his face and began making baby sounds to him clearly relieved that he was okay.

The nurse came into us on our arrival. 'Hello,' she said cheerily. 'It's lucky you both came back now because we are just about to take your wee man away again for his scan. The results of his lumbar puncture are not back yet, but we will go ahead and do his scan now before the staff leave for the night. '

We didn't ask how our baby was during the lumbar puncture. I knew.

We were allowed to stay in the tiny cubicle while the scan was being performed on Ryan. There was no pain involved in that. A short time later, the nurse returned with Ryan in her arms again. I took him from her as she entered the cubicle.

He was agitated and crying. I took the soother from his baby bag and popped it into his mouth. He sucked ferociously on it in an attempt to fill his empty stomach. I began to rock him in my arms when I noticed the small bandage plastered on the back of his hand. I looked at the nurse, pointing to it.

'It's okay,' she said, reading my thoughts. 'We just took a little blood for a sample. Now the doctor will be around to see you both again in a few minutes with the information about the scan. Is that okay?' she questioned.

'Yes,' we said in unison.

'Nurse.' I stopped her before she left the cubicle. 'Our baby is hungry.'

'Don't worry,' she said, smiling. 'We will be putting an intravenous drip in with nutrients and fluids shortly. It will sustain him for now. We won't let your baby starve. I promise,' she said and left.

I wanted to tell her that my baby was starving, such was my frustration. Four weeks ago, we were a happy, contented family at home with our beautiful, healthy baby boy. What just happened to our world?

Dessie took over rocking Ryan in his arms in an attempt to settle him down while I held the soother in his mouth. He was beginning to get sleepy when the doctor came into the cubicle to talk with us. I took Ryan from my husband and lay him in his cot gently. He fell asleep, sucking hard on the soother. We sat down with the doctor sitting facing us as before.

I felt a bit like a rat in a trap sitting there waiting to be pounced on.

The cubicle was so tiny.

'Well,' the doctor began to talk, clasping his hands together. 'We have found the problem.'

I held my breath.

My husband grasped my hand tightly.

'Your baby has what's medically called pyloric stenosis.'

My mouth gaped open automatically. Dessie and I exchanged a bewildered look at each other.

'I see you don't know what that means by your expressions.' The doctor giggled.

We sat stunned.

'Firstly, it's not serious or life-threatening. '

We let out a sigh of pure relief.

'What it is, is a thickening of the muscle that goes from the stomach to the small intestine, which meant that your baby's food could not pass through the muscle and lodged there, which inevitably caused his vomiting.'

'Can you fix it, Doctor?' I blurted out in anticipation.

'Yes,' he nodded as he answered. 'We can, and it's actually quite common in newborn babies.'

'Is it, Doctor?' Dessie asked, stunned. 'I'd never heard of it,' he said, looking at me for inspiration.

I shook my head. 'Me either,' I said. We both looked at the doctor again.

'Well, you can take my word for it.' He smiled, then continued explaining. 'What we need to do is make a small incision in the wall of the muscle to open a channel from the stomach to the small intestine so that the food can pass through. We will perform this pyloromyotomy, which is the medical term for the surgery, in the morning, probably around 10 o'clock or so. Afterwards, your baby will be right as rain. His vomiting will cease.' The doctor slapped his hands together in a show of victory.

Dessie and I both wept with joy. At the back of my mind, though, was the concern that my baby had to have surgery. I gathered myself. 'Doctor,' I said in a concerned tone. 'Is the surgery straight forward?'

He nodded as he said, 'Yes, it's a common complaint. As I said, we perform this procedure regularly. It will only take approximately an hour. Afterwards, we will monitor how well your baby is at keeping down his food for twenty-four hours and then you can take him home.'

Those words were music to our ears.

'That's great, Doctor. Thank you,' my husband said, barely able to contain his joy and relief that our baby boy was going to be alright.

Before the doctor left, he turned to us. 'By the way,' he said. 'I just want to let you know that the lumbar puncture we performed showed up clear of any brain virus, and also that this condition, pyloric stenosis may be hereditary, although we are not certain of it. Did either of you have this condition as babies?'

Dessie and I looked at each other and then shook our heads at the doctor.

'We've never even heard of it, Doctor,' I replied.

'That's fine, he said. 'I just wanted to let you know.'

'Doctor,' I said, stopping him as he was leaving. 'If this is hereditary, would there be a chance that if we have other children, they could develop this as well?'

The doctor puffed out a sigh as he contemplated his answer. 'It's common in first-born baby boys. I have had no experience of a second child of a family developing it, so I'll have to say it's very unlikely.'

'That's fine, Doctor. Thank you,' I said

The nurse came into the cubicle just after the doctor left and explained that she needed to put an IV into Ryan to get fluids and other nutrients into him. 'This may be unpleasant for you two to watch,' she said sympathetically. 'Would you like to go for a coffee and return in about fifteen minutes or so?'

We nodded agreeably.

When we arrived back to Ryan, he was tubed up with the IV attached to the needle on the back of his tiny hand. It was bandaged around the area. The nurse said it had to be done that way in case Ryan pulled it out while fidgeting.

Our baby was restless and crying. He was hungry. I lifted him into my arms gently and began to rock him in my arms, popping the soother in his mouth to try to satisfy him. Dessie and I shared rocking him in our arms until eventually, he fell asleep. As I was putting him back down in his cot, the nurse appeared and told us that it would not be practical or necessary for us to stay with our baby tonight.

'We will be keeping a close eye on him,' she assured us. 'And since he won't be getting any bottle-feeds, there really is no reason for you to try and sleep in this tiny room. Go home you both and get some well-needed rest tonight,' she said kindly.

We were unsure and reluctant to leave our baby boy, but the nurse sensing our concern assured us that we could phone during the night any time. Reiterating that it was futile for us to stay. We relented and at 10 pm that Saturday night, we kissed our baby boy goodnight and left, telling the night nurse that we would be up early in the morning.

It was the hardest thing in the world, leaving our son that night. There was an eerie silence in our home without our baby. This fact filled me with the awareness that for such a tiny person, our baby's presence in our heart and our home life had a huge impact on me. There was a void in my very existence that night in our home.

After a restless night for both of us, we were back up in the baby ward at the hospital at 8 am the next morning. As we were about to enter Ryan's small cubicle, the day nurse stopped us by putting her arm out in a motion to tell us not to enter. We stopped dead in our tracks. I immediately felt my head go light.

'Everything is okay with Ryan, don't worry,' she said urgently to calm us. She motioned us close to the nurses' station. 'I just need to tell you both before you go in that we had to put another IV into your baby. 'She paused before continuing. 'He pulled the one in his hand out during the night. He is fine,' she said, looking at me as she put her hand gently on my arm. 'The thing is we could not find a vein substantial enough to put another IV in his wee hands, so we had to put it in his forehead.'

My heart was thumping. Dessie and I looked at each other in shocked silence.

'Don't get upset when you see him,' the nurse urged us. 'We had to tie his hands outstretched to the back of his cot. This is the only way to prevent him from pulling the IV out when he fidgets. It looks worse than it is.' She came close to our faces as she said this. Her eyes widened as she looked at us.

We had no response for her, except to nod as we pushed past her in anticipation of seeing our baby boy. Immediately, I moaned as my hand went to my mouth at the sight of my baby. I heard Dessie sigh in a melancholy tone.

Ryan had the IV needle smack in the middle of his forehead with a plaster each side. His wee arms outstretched each side of him with what looked like an elasticated bandage covering each hand and tied separately above his head, to each side of his cot. He lay wide awake contentedly staring at the ceiling.

My heart ached with pity for my beautiful baby boy. Tears welled up.

Dessie came to me and put his arm around my shoulder. 'Mary,' he said quietly. 'I know it's hard to look at our wee man like this, but it's for his own good.'

I breathed in a sigh and reached down to kiss Ryan. He wriggled around, clearly uncomfortable being restricted. At that moment, I was eternally grateful that he was too young to understand what was going on for him.

48 hours later on 18 November 1994, we had our baby boy home. Everything went smoothly during his surgery, and he was holding down his food. No vomiting, as the doctor had predicted.

We had to start him off gradually on his feeds, and by the end of that week, he was on his full volume of ounces once again. We were completely overjoyed at his recuperation, although something had changed in me as his mother. I became obsessively overprotective of him for several months. I found myself constantly checking on him while he slept. Even though I knew his vomiting had been eliminated by the surgery, I still tensed up while winding him after his feeds, until I came to the acceptance in my own time that he was going to be okay.

During those months following Ryan's surgery, I had a phone call one day from the floor manager of the textile company where I had worked the previous year. He had set up another small textile factory to produce kiddies tracksuits and wondered would I come on board for a year or so to help out sewing them.

I thanked him but declined, explaining that I could not leave my baby to go to work at this time. He understood and asked me if it would be an option for me to work from home for him? This I agreed to. I phoned my mother asking her if she would be interested in coming to my home for a few hours a day to watch Ryan for me while I worked. I would give her a wage also. I was shocked by her response. She was elated about this

'Aw, Mary, love, I'd love that. A wee job of my own after all these years. I'm delighted you asked me.'

When she said these words I was overwhelmed with pity for her; with the realisation that she had devoted practically her whole life to being a mother to us, never having the freedom to have an outside interest or job; restricting herself mentally and physically to being a mother first and foremost. So that now in her early sixties, she did not have the social skills or confidence to begin a life outside in the world. My mother literally gave her life to us, preventing herself from ever having financial stability in a career or job.

She never had the companionship of another man after my father left her either. Even though she was only in her early thirties then and a very attractive woman. Her kids were her life. Her sacrifices, and strength of character, her authenticity as a human being, humble me beyond words. She will have my admiration and loyalty to my dying day.

That spell of my working from home lasted a year until my manager's orders were completed. It was a lovely time for my mam and me. We both got enormous pleasure from working together in my home. When Ryan was sleeping, Mam would help me in my work by cutting threads and folding the tracksuits. She loved her wee job, and I was extremely grateful to her and fulfilled with the knowledge that she was happy.

Just as my work at home was coming to an end, my nana's health began to deteriorate. She was still her witty self, but her memory was getting worse. Her appetite was also ebbing. It was a painful time for my mother.

She would put my son in the pram and take a walk up to see nana. The nursing home was close to where I lived. My nana passed away in her sleep in May 1995, the year after my son was born. It was a sad time for everyone who knew this wonderful woman. It was bittersweet for my mother, for the woman she'd known as her mother had gone long before she died. My mother was relieved that nanna did not have to endure much more.

On 9 January 1999, at the age of 31, I gave birth to our second son. That pure unconditional love rose in me once again. He weighed eight pounds and ten ounces, and he was beautiful.

We named him Liam. Ryan was now four years old and doted on his baby brother.

All the while during my baby's first few weeks in this world, I had a sense of dread when I was feeding him. I think this was because I had a stark, frightening remembrance of Ryan's vomiting when he was that age but even more than that, I had a kind of instinctive urge to be wary when feeding him. I have no idea why I felt that way as the doctor did tell us that it was very unlikely I would have another baby with the same problem. Yet I was worried. Our baby boy was showing no signs of vomiting, but I simply couldn't shake the knowing instinctive feeling. When I mentioned my fears to my husband, he also reiterated what the doctor had said, telling me not to be worried. I worried none the less. As it turned out, I was justified in my instinct.

One day when Liam was four weeks old, I felt the familiar contracting of his rib cage as I sat him up to relieve his wind after his bottle. It was a midweek morning, and our son Ryan was at school. Immediately after, Liam began to vomit forcefully and, as with Ryan, it was projectile, shooting across the floor in the kitchen where I sat with him on my lap in our home. As with Ryan, it only lasted a minute but had the same volume, and Liam was fine afterwards.

I sat cuddling my baby in despair, having now full knowledge of what was wrong and the awareness of what he would also have to endure. There was no doubt in my mind after witnessing his vomiting that my second baby boy also had pyloric stenosis. I cried silently for a minute or two.

Gathering myself then, I quite calmly set about washing and changing my baby, all the while planning, in my head, the arrangements we would have to make to spend time in the hospital with our second baby boy. My first phone call was to my GP. After telling her Liam's symptoms and given Ryan's history, she told me to call when I could and pick up a letter to bring to the accident and emergency department at the hospital. I then phoned my husband.

He was momentarily silent in shock. 'Are you sure it's the same kind of vomiting, Mary?' he questioned, not wanting to believe that his second baby boy would have to have surgery also.

'Yes, Dessie,' I said calmly. 'I'm certain.'

'But the doctor said –,' he began.

I interrupted him midway. 'Dessie, it doesn't matter what the doctor said. He did not say there was definitely no chance of another son having it. He only said he had no experience of it. Dessie,' I continued. 'Liam has pyloric stenosis also. I'm absolutely sure of it, and I want him fixed as soon as possible. I can't let him go through what Ryan went through.'

My husband relented. 'Okay,' he said in a deflated voice. 'I'll get cover at work and be home in the hour.'

'That's fine, love,' I said. 'I'll phone Mam and ask her to come up and stay with Ryan.'

My mother was horrified when I told her. 'Aw the poor wee fella,' she said sympathetically.

'I know, Mam,' I said as I was putting our baby's toiletries and food into the baby bag to bring up to the hospital.

'The girls and I were talking about it before I came up.'

My mother was referring to my sisters. They had both phoned me earlier when they'd heard the news from my mother.

'For the life of us, Mary, we can't figure out where this pyl –. What is it called again? I can't even pronounce it,' she said in frustration.

'It's called pyloric stenosis, Mam.'

'Oh, aye. Well, anyway, it's never been heard of in our family, Mags. Didn't you say it's inherited?'

'I said it might be, Mam.'

'What about Luke? Did you ask him if he ever heard of it?'

Luke was my father-in-law's name. 'Yes, Mam, we did,' I said beginning to get frustrated myself.

Mam was sitting at the kitchen table in our home with Ryan on her lap, colouring pictures with him. 'And what did he say about it?' she asked.

She was relentless in her curiosity about who'd given our baby pyloric stenosis. I sighed. 'He said the same as you just said, Mam. He never heard of it either. He did say though,' I continued. 'That its likely babies died from that way back in the generations and nobody ever knew they had it.'

Dessie's father lived in town about 2 miles from our home. He was in his early seventies then. He, like my mother and sisters, was blown over when we explained about the pyloric stenosis and how it may be hereditary.

Everybody's reaction was the same. 'What is it called? Say that again? Never heard of it.' All of them wide-eyed with confusion and bewilderment. My mother even asked me to write the name pyloric stenosis down on a piece of paper for her so that she could show it to her friends when they asked her about Ryan.

'I'll never remember those words, Mags,' she said, annoyed.

My mother insisted it came from my husband's side of the family, and my father-in-law was convinced it had to come from my side. The debating society had been in full swing four years ago about pyloric stenosis and who was to blame when Ryan was diagnosed. With my mother waving her piece of paper with the name of it to all her pals in her community and my father-in-law looking at my husband and me in total confusion.

'Are you sure it's called that?' he said, almost doubting that we had heard the doctor properly.

Now here we were on the same merry go round. We kissed Ryan goodbye and thanked Mam for taking care of him. We were at the hospital by three in the afternoon that day. Our baby boy was admitted straight away, and when the doctor heard about my first-born son having pyloric stenosis, they scanned Liam within the hour.

As I had suspected, he did have pyloric stenosis. Thankfully, he did not have to endure the pain and discomfort of a lumbar puncture or the excessive vomiting that our poor son Ryan suffered.

Liam was put on to an IV drip immediately and booked to have the pyloromyotomy surgery done early the next morning. The doctor told us that they would do Liam's surgery cosmetically.

I asked him what he meant.

'Well,' he said. 'Does your other son have a scar?'

'Yes,' I said. 'It's a small scar about two inches in length just above his belly button,' I replied confused.

'This time, your baby won't have a scar,' he said proudly. 'We will make the incision around the edge of his belly button. It won't be noticeable at all.'

'Okay, thanks, Doctor,' I said in an indifferent tone. I really did not care about a tiny scar on my baby's belly. I only wanted my baby back to health and home with us again.

Two days later we brought our baby Liam home pyloric stenosis free and back to full health.

***

My life now was in a steady flow for the next few years into my early thirties. It mostly consisted of taking care of our boys and running the home while my husband worked. During those years, we had made friends with the other parents in our street whose children were around the same age as ours.

We socialised together at weekends. Sarah and Katie and I were close in age and had become close friends. We spent a lot of time together. Sarah was a stay-at-home mother like me then, and Katie was studying from home for her degree as a lab technician.

Because our children were so young, we would take turns inviting each other to our homes on a Friday or Saturday night and take the children with us. This worked perfectly for all of us, as the kids would play together in their rooms while we parents would sit and have a few drinks and light food in the kitchen. I looked so forward to these social nights. They became a big part of my weekly life. My children kept me grounded. They were my world. They needed me, and that felt good.

I regularly visited my siblings and my mother. We remained very close, and my mother's house was still a hive of activity on a daily basis and now with grandchildren. My sisters Erin and Lizzy and my brother Joseph still lived in our childhood housing estate, so Mammy got plenty of visitors in her day. I found comfort in that because I hated the thought of Mammy ever being alone. I'm not sure why, but I always held a sense of pity for her.

One particular day, I was visiting my sister Erin, and we began to reminisce about childhood. We started to talk about Daddy. 'I was talking to Dermot, Mary,' my sister said. Dermot was one of our half-brothers.

We had been told a long time ago that Daddy had met another woman. This news was not given to us by my mother personally.

As we got older and circulated socially more, we heard about my father's double life on the streets basically, and from friends and relations also. We all knew there were other children too. Again, my mother never discussed anything about Dad's other life and family with us. Nor did we look to her for any information about Daddy. It was always a touchy subject to bring up with Mammy. Her demeanour would change instantly when we mentioned his name. There was a mix of anger and sadness in her eyes, and she would shrug any comment off and change the subject. Or she would simply say, 'Don't ask me any questions about your daddy, child. I don't know anything about him. Now, that's final.'

The news of Daddy's life and new family had no real impact on me personally because I already knew and all my siblings simply shrugged it off. This was because the reality was that our dad was not in our lives long enough for any of us to bond with or develop any relationship with him. Well, not us younger ones anyway.

The three older siblings, Lizzy, Joseph, and Ciaran, did have Dad as a caring father when they were little. Just like the rest of us, though we all seemed to just carry on with our lives as if he had never been part of us at all.

'Dermot told me that Daddy has not been well recently,' my sister continued. 'It's his heart. He has problems with fluid.'

I was silent. I didn't know how to absorb this information, or how I was expected to feel. Suddenly, I said, 'Would you like to meet Daddy, Erin?'

My sister stared at me for a moment in silence. 'I don't know,' she then replied. 'How about you?'

'I don't know either. It just came to my mind there.'

Ironically, a couple of weeks after this conversation, my sister phoned to tell me that Daddy had been taken to hospital. My half-brother had phoned her. It wasn't good. His heart was failing. My first thought was 'Why do I feel nothing getting this news?' I was numb, but not with shock. I simply had no emotion at all. I suppose it stands to reason. I had no love, yet no hate either. Only nothingness! It was a strange time for me.

My father died in hospital. He was sixty-eight years old. We never got up to see him. It all happened too fast for us.

It was a turbulent time for us as a family. Since we had no part in our daddy's life in the latter years, it was hard for us to pull together. My mother stayed out of any conversations about Daddy's funeral. She did not want to give any opinion or advice on the subject.

As I sat in her house having tea around this time, I plucked up the courage to mention the funeral to her. 'Mam,' I said nervously. 'I'm unsure about whether to go to Dad's funeral or not.'

My mother turned to look at me with an expressionless face. 'Mary,' she said. 'He was your daddy, not mine. You all need to decide for yourselves what you would like to do as his children. I won't be getting involved in this.' Her piercing blue eyes bore into mine as she said these words. I knew she meant business then, and I felt pity for her. She showed no emotion, yet this was the man she'd married and shared many happy years with. I often wonder, did she shed tears when she was alone at night? Did she grieve for the love she'd once known?

We were all in contact with each other on the phone. It was an upsetting time for all of us. My eldest brother, especially, wanted to be part of Dad's wake and funeral. He'd stayed in contact with my father through the years.

They were both lorry drivers and used to meet regularly at customs and excise offices. They did share a father-son relationship. He had feelings for Dad and wanted to be a part of his wake and funeral,

I felt sorry for him. He was in contact with me on the phone, and I felt that we should go as a family, all of us together, to Dad's wake. I then took it upon myself to phone all the siblings, asking them would they be a part of the funeral, which was not my place to do nor my duty. Unfortunately, my siblings had their own thoughts around what they felt was right for them. Some of them simply wanted no part in Dads' funeral or wake. They had long stopped thinking of my dad being any part of their lives. My two younger brothers didn't even remember him, so his death meant nothing to them, naturally enough.

This left me feeling angry and critical of them. In hindsight, I now know and am very aware that this behaviour was yet another flaw in my character. To my mind, if they did not see my reasoning as the proper way to think, then they were wrong, even though I understood their reservations. I wanted them to see things as I did. So, ultimately, it all left me feeling resentful.

You see, where I lacked confidence to be assertive in the outside world, I doubled up on it when it came to my own door with my siblings. I needed to accept that my siblings had a right to do whatever they wanted.

That said, so did I. With that thought in mind, I lay in bed thinking. I hadn't seen my father in years and began to wonder what he looked like. I knew he had stopped drinking in the latter years of his life, and spent most of his time in his garage fixing cars and lorries. Our half-brother and sister told us this. Dad had isolated himself a lot now. I began to wonder what his thoughts were as regards us, his kids. I began to visualise him deep in thoughts of remorse and guilt. It made me sad. I began to pity him.

This was the way my mind worked, on over-drive, when there was any trauma. I would start to dramatise situations. In any case, with these feelings that arose in me that night, also came a tremendous urge to see my father once again. I suddenly craved to hold his hand and kiss him goodbye for once and for all. I needed closure.

The next morning, I phoned my mother. I was nervous because I knew talking about all this Daddy business was very upsetting for her.

'Ma?' I said when she answered. 'Would you be okay with me if I went to Dad's wake? I just want to see his face before they bury him.' My voice was shaky. 'Ma, I won't if you don't want me to.'

There was silence for a moment on the line, and I was holding my breath. Then my mother began to speak in a quiet calm voice

'Mary, you go to see your daddy. I can't feel what you feel, but I understand. Go with my blessing but remember, don't expect your brothers and sisters to feel the same way as you do.'

My mother knew me so well. It's as if she could read my thoughts.

'Leave them alone, Mary. Let them make their own choices.'

'Okay, Mam, I will,' I promised.

'Oh, and one more thing, love, do me one favour,' she said. 'Please, don't take a drink off anyone at your daddy's wake.'

This statement stunned me. 'No, Ma, of course, I won't,' I replied.

'Okay, love,' she said. 'Take care'.

After I hung up from the conversation with my mother, I was puzzled a bit. Why had Mam said that to me? When I reflect now, I realise why. My mother knew all about me and my insecurities.

How fear and anxiety plagued me in uncertain territories, which this certainly was. She was also very aware that I used alcohol to relieve me of this. She did not want the other family to see me drinking. Nobody knew me better than my mother.

That same evening, my eldest brother Patrick, his wife Josie and my older sister Erin arrived at Dad's house. The rest of our siblings chose not to. Our half-siblings greeted us politely and took us to the room Dad was laid out in. I was very nervous. We all were a bit.

I looked at my father's face as he lay there, and that pity rose in me again. I was sad. He had changed a lot. His hair had receded and thinned. When he'd been at home with us, he'd had a great big head of curls and a few tiny ringlets that used to hang down over his forehead into his eyes. His face was thin too. Actually, except for his huge hands, I could not see any resemblance to the man I knew at all.

I put my hand on his hand then surprisingly, to myself, I began to cry silently. The tears came from nowhere. I bent down and kissed my father on the forehead and whispered, 'Goodbye, Daddy.'

I thought back to the conversation I'd had with my sister a couple of weeks previously and wondered if we had missed out on an opportunity to get back into Dad's life. Maybe we should have pursued the idea of meeting him again. Just afterwards, another thought came to me. Perhaps, meeting Dad would not have been very wise. He may not have had the answers we wanted to hear to the questions we wanted to ask.

Later that night as I lay awake in bed, my thoughts turned to my father, to the role he held in my life. I began to slowly draw out my memories of him from where they were stashed at the back of my mind. As I did this, a picture was starting to develop for me of what kind of a person my father was really like, his identity. I began to piece together my own personal experiences of him along with details my mother had given me in my adult life.

On rare occasions, while spending quiet time with my mother in her home, we would happen on to the subject of her and Dad in the early years of their marriage. It had been while they lived in London with my aunt Cecilia, who had died in the late 80s.

I was always intrigued when my mother began to open up about Dad and her together because we as their children knew so little about their life together since Dad left. One day, Mam was talking about her sister Cecilia, and I decided I would probe her gently to talk about her time living over there. I had to be very careful. My mother had long since made it very clear to us as we were growing up, not to question her about our daddy. I believe she held a terrible resentment towards him, and understandably so. I also believe Mammy wanted to protect us from being in contact with Dad. She knew his character. We did not.

However, as the years passed, we all grew up and made our own way in life. My mother had then fewer responsibilities for our welfare; this mellowed her a bit with regards to talking openly to us about Dad. I knew my mother and father had lived in London for a couple of years when they got married. My father had been offered work there on the building sites. That was in the 1950s.

'Mam,' I said, as she had finished telling me a tale about my aunt, Cecilia. 'You and Dad were happily married then, weren't you?' I was nervous about her reaction to my question.

'Oh yes, love, we were.'

I sighed with relief. She seemed quite content to reminisce with me at that time.

'We lived in the same building as your aunt, Cecilia, and uncle, Oscar. We lived on the ground floor, and they lived above us.' My mother stopped talking momentarily as she seemed to be gathering her thoughts.

I stayed silent.

'You know, Mary,' she continued. 'Your father was a very hard worker. He never missed a day's work. Even if he was sick with flu, he went to his work, and he never touched a drink in those days.'

'That's good, Mam,' was all I could say in the hope that she would keep talking. I looked into her face as I sat beside her on the sofa. She had a dreamy look in her eyes.

'Yes,' she said. 'We were very happy for many years but when you kids came along things started to change. Your daddy always wanted he and I to go places together alone.' Mam avoided my stare as she said this to me, almost embarrassed. 'He just couldn't seem to understand why I wanted to stay at home with my children, instead of getting a babysitter to go out every weekend, or go for weekends to your uncle Pierse in Dublin.'

Pierse was my dad's brother who lived there.

'Oh really, Mam,' I said sympathetically. 'That must have been hard for you to deal with.'

'Yes,' she replied forlornly. 'We had many rows. Then your dad started drinking heavy.' Mam stopped talking abruptly, then sighed. 'Mary, love, your father didn't want to grow up, he was like Peter Pan.'

On that note, she got up from the sofa and turned to me. 'Do you want another cuppa, love?' she asked.

'Yes, I will, Mam. Thanks.'

I knew then I would not get any more information; subject closed.

That night after saying goodbye to my father, I lay in bed and began to accumulate this information into my memories of Daddy. I was trying to piece together the puzzle of my father's identity, moreover, the reason why he did not make any effort to be in our, his children's, lives.

Sleep evaded me by then, so I got up and went to the kitchen to make myself a cup of tea. As I sat in the quiet of the night at my kitchen table, my mind still whirled.

This happened to me frequently throughout my life; these waves of curiosity as to my father's feelings for me and indeed for all my siblings; particularly since I have had children of my own.

I would witness my husband with his sons, his devotion to them. The pride and joy he felt for them was clear for all to see. His sons were his world. He would give his life gladly for them. No person takes precedence in my husband Dessie's heart over his boys, including me.

Witnessing that unconditional love he has for them, I would sometimes think of Daddy. On rare occasions, I was even a touch envious of my sons to have been given this selfless affection from their daddy. I had never had that.

Then I would wonder again 'why'? These thoughts always reflected in my mood when I dwelt upon them, making me resentful and full of self-pity, so I forced the questions out of my thoughts, putting them as always to the back of my mind.

However that night as I sat in my kitchen, I was beginning to see a different view of things. For some reason unknown to me, I was being open-minded about my dad. I found myself thinking that perhaps there was a reason for his absence in our lives. Sentences began to form in my thoughts.

Perhaps, as my mother had pointed out, my father could not be the responsible person he was required to be, as a husband and father. Perhaps, he simply did not have the skills. As I accepted these thoughts as a possibility, I began to get flashbacks of my father again in my childhood years. His jolly laughter as he came into our home, shouting and singing at the top of his voice, calling our names out from the bottom of the stairs as we slept.

He wanted us up to sing songs regardless of the time of night, or if we had school the next day. I could remember my mother's pleas to him not to wake us being totally disregarded. I could hear him bellowing.

'Ah sure, Evie. I bought this lemonade for the childer.' His slang word for children. 'Let them come down. I'll play my harmonica, and we will have a sing-song.'

As I recalled these images in my mind, I smiled slightly at his child-like behaviour. Of course, he was drunk on these few occasions. We were used to that. More and more memories began to flood my mind; events I had long forgotten about.

In my mind, I was slowly getting a clear picture of my father. I put my cup down and sighed. 'Aw, Dad,' I found myself saying. 'What were you like?'

Just then, another long-lost memory came to mind. We were at a beach. I remember putting my bathing suit on in Daddy's car and my siblings and I paddling in the water. My mammy putting her arms around my daddy to help him into the shallow water for a paddle. I remembered us laughing as Daddy groaned in fear of touching the water in his bare feet.

These images flooded my mind with no warning. I put my head in my hands in an effort to clear my thinking. As I did so, a sentence formed in my thoughts. My daddy was afraid. As I lifted my head up again, I was taken aback with the clarity of what all these meant for me.

Yet another memory came to my mind then. It was a conversation between my eldest brother Patrick and I from years ago before I had my children. He was telling me in my kitchen that he had been talking to Dad at the customs and excise office they frequented as lorry drivers.

He said that Dad asked him how we all are and how Mammy was. My father told Patrick that he thinks about us all the time. I could clearly remember me saying to Patrick, 'Sure, why does he not try to see us then, Patrick?'

Patrick replied, 'Dad said he is afraid to get in touch with us cause it might upset Mam.'

My reply was, 'That's a cop out, Patrick.'

Patrick shrugged in response.

As I reminisced over all these events, memories and conversations, I was suddenly impacted with an instinctive inner knowledge of who my father was. His personality seemed to shine through my consciousness. The puzzle was complete.

I saw that, like me, fear had a strong hold on him. I realised that that fear capped with his seeming inability to mature mentally enough to be a responsible adult, along with his alcoholic drinking, led me to my final conclusions about my father.

I truly believed there and then that my father simply did not have the capacity emotionally or mentally to live up to his responsibilities, or to people's expectations of him in life. My mother was right; Daddy never grew up.

This sudden awareness had a positive impact on me that night because I finally saw my father in a different light, although his behaviour could not be excused.

I began to believe that his fears, his lack of coping skills, and obvious powerlessness over alcohol, had forced him to choose the way he lived. Mountains of bitterness and feelings of rejection towards my father, crumbled from my heart as this revelation unfolded before my eyes.

That night, alone in the silence, I found myself saying, my daddy did love me in as much as he was capable of giving love. I sat back and let out a long sigh. As I did so, another long-forgotten memory came to me. Daddy was kneeling at my bedside. I began to remember the smell of alcohol vividly from his breath as he kissed me on the forehead, then tucked the blanket around my chin and left the room.

That night of intense awakening had an uplifting effect on my confidence. I found the answers to my questions, at last, for me, personally.

When you grow up with a daddy who breezes in and out of your life, as my siblings and I had, it leaves you very confused and unsure of what your daddy means for you.

We, Daddy's children, had the added humiliation of being told by our community that our daddy had a new family.

I talk for myself as I say here that the knowledge of this left me feeling unloved by my daddy, which led to me questioning why this was. Since there was no answer to that question for me as a child, I formed my own opinion.

Perhaps I wasn't good enough for my father's love. Obviously, a naïve conclusion to conjure up, but as a child, I could only form a black or white answer to my question. Since there was nobody to explain why Daddy was not there, I had to come up with some reason.

On that night of my father's wake in the silence of my home, I became filled with the awareness that Dad's absence from my life was nothing personal against me as his daughter. The problem lay with him, not me.

It seemed for me that saying goodbye to my father had opened up a Pandora's Box in my consciousness. I found that resentment was being replaced by pity for him, for what he'd missed out on in life with his children and his grandchildren whom he never even got to know.

The place in my heart which had once held only bitterness towards him was now being replaced with sympathy. Where there was anger and judgement of him, I now began to feel empathy for his underlying fears and the twisted thinking they provoked since I too could identify with these.

I can never assume to speak on behalf of my siblings as regard to how they perceive our dad. Nor have I discussed my thoughts about his behaviour to them; that's not my right. I can only speak for what was instinctively evolving emotionally for me on that night as I sat alone in my home.

I was looking at my father's life with an open mind and heart for the first time. I began to identify with him rather than condemn him. It was enlightening but also sad. As these revelations naturally came upon me, I was aware that my father had spent the last ten years of his life mostly isolated in his home and his garage where he was doing mechanics for friends' cars. Our half-brother Dermot had told us this when we'd met him socially through the years.

Dad had also quit drinking and had even started attending church. Knowing this, I began picturing him in my imagination alone; perhaps reflecting on his life just as I had often seen my mother do. Remembering the sadness in her eyes as she spoke of happy times with Dad.

I realised then that my father was not made of stone. Surely, he, like everyone else, had his moments of sadness, guilt, remorse, and possibly regret. With these thoughts, my pity for him grew. Tears welled up in my eyes as they grew heavy and tired. I rose from the kitchen chair and went upstairs to bed, as I lay down and closed my eyes to sleep, I found myself saying, 'Dad, I forgive you. I hope you can rest in peace'.

***

Two years later, at age thirty-two, I found out I was pregnant with our third child. We were very happy. One day, early into my pregnancy, we were visiting my mother-in-law's grave. She had been just forty-two when she died. My husband had been in his early twenties. I never had the pleasure of knowing her.

Dessie's dad was alive then and a big part of our lives. My husband had one brother, his name was Martin, and he was four years younger than my husband.

While we were walking back to the car, I felt a severe cramp in my lower stomach. It passed quite quickly, so I made no remark of it to my husband. But, when we got home, I had another and then another in quick succession and more severe.

I was miscarrying our baby. When I realised, I told my husband. He started to panic.

'Will we go to the hospital? I'll drive. Or will we call an ambulance?' he was splurting.

I knew there was no need for the hospital. The pregnancy was over. I had lost our baby.

'No,' I said calmly to him. 'It's fine. There is no need. It's over.' It was as final as that for both of us. No comforting each other, and no tears. All that was between us was an awkwardness. I had no show of emotion, good, bad or indifferent. The only solid emotion I can name for how I felt then was disappointment.

My husband was very uneasy around me for a while after that. He sensed by my demeanour that I was a closed book where the miscarriage was concerned. It was the coping skill I used. The one I was familiar with. Without analysing it, I wiped the episode out of my mind.

In hindsight, the reality was that I did not want to process the fact that my baby had died. The pregnancy was over before it had begun, for me. It was only much later in life that my husband and I mentioned the miscarriage, and even then, very briefly, and to be honest, I never asked my husband how he felt about it. I think I had acquired a special technique to put the bad times away in the dark crevices of my mind. Pretend they never happened. That was my coping skill. A very dangerous one, I was yet to find out.

* * *

I had my sons, my family, and my friends. Most of the time I was happy, although there were nights when I lay in bed while everyone slept and I would yearn, for what I'm not sure. It was a nameless void inside. I tried to brush it away regularly.

On 13 November 2001, I gave birth to our third son, a big bouncing baby boy. He came into the world weighing nine pounds and ten ounces, and he was beautiful. Again, that familiar surge of pure love rose in me. We named him Danny.

My husband and I were very proud and grateful. These three beautiful children I had been blessed with were my world, my rainbows.

When feeding our new baby son, Danny, I didn't feel any tension or fear of him vomiting, or the instinctive dread I had felt after feeding Liam as a baby, just over three years ago.

Perhaps this was because he was such a big baby, filling out three- to six-month baby suits from birth. I'm not sure but, in any case, the horror of the vomiting ordeal we went through with our other sons was on my mind. For that reason, I took him over to our GP for a letter to have him scanned at the hospital when he was three weeks old. My doctor willingly gave me a letter but felt that there was very little chance that my third son could have pyloric stenosis also.

I acknowledged her doubts but took the letter and made arrangements to bring Danny to the hospital to have his scan done. I needed to put my mind at rest and save my third baby from enduring any projectile vomiting if he did have it.

With a sigh of relief, my husband and I thanked the doctor when he told us Danny was pyloric stenosis free.

The following year in 2002, my husband's father's health began to deteriorate. He'd suffered from rheumatoid arthritis for years. As he got older in years, his condition worsened. He had two hip replacements; the first when he was seventy years old in 1996 and the other, two years later, when he was seventy-two.

For as long as I had known my husband, his father Luke had been suffering from this debilitating painful bone disease.

He never let it hold him back from enjoying life, and we had many trips and spent fun-filled nights with him. He was a devoted father and grandfather to our boys, but unfortunately, as his arthritis worsened and spread, it took away his mobility as it was too painful for him to get around. It was harrowing for my husband Dessie and his brother Martin watching him suffer.

Luke had remarried in 1994 when he was in his late sixties. His new wife Ann had never married, and they met each other through a mutual friend. Sadly, his arthritis seemed to worsen rapidly after they'd become husband and wife.

For three years from that year 2002, to his death on New Year's Eve 2005, my father-in-law had been practically housebound, and in constant pain. Dessie would go to see him every day and always came home from visiting melancholy and in a low mood. Such was his despair witnessing his beloved dad, failing and in constant pain.

It was torture for him looking at his father suffering so much, for his wife Ann also and Dessie's brother.

Luke was a wonderful father to my husband and his brother. He had been a huge part of their daily lives since their mother died, and a loved and cherished grandfather to our boys. His death had a huge emotional impact on my husband Dessie and indeed, on all of us. He will always be sadly missed.

During my mid to late thirties, the financial responsibilities were getting bigger with our sons now in school. I decided to return to work. I applied for a job as a sales assistant in a local boutique and was offered the job. My manager kindly gave me hours that suited school hours.

I loved the job and was very soon promoted to visual merchandiser, which gave me the responsibility of outfit building. This entails complimenting skirts and trousers with the appropriate colour tops, handbags, and fashion jewellery, on all the display rails and the shop window. This was a whole new experience for me. It was the first time in my working life that I felt important in my role.

To rise for work every morning with no inhibitions, no fears, to be relaxed and full of anticipation for what lay ahead each day was completely foreign for me. Working there filled me with new confidence and enthusiasm. It was exhilarating. To be honest, I was amazed at myself.

There were intervals early on in my employment when I would fumble. That caused me huge embarrassment, and I would blush, but my boss and co-worker were very understanding and helpful. My awkwardness soon faded away. I did my job with a smile on my face every day fearlessly. I had come home at last. Thirty-odd years into my life, I had finally started to believe in myself.

I thought of my mother's words to me all those years ago. 'Mary, love, you will grow out of it.'

I must be a very slow learner!

Perhaps being a mother contributed to my transformation. I was now in the role of teaching my sons to believe in themselves and have confidence in everything they do. Clearly, for most people starting out in a simple job like this would not seem to be any challenge but believe me, it was a huge hurdle for me, especially the social aspect of the job.

For the majority of the years I had worked in the textile factory, I had felt like I was holding my breath every day because of my shyness, lack of social skills, and confidence. Although I still suffered bouts of feeling unsure of myself, I had matured enough to push past them.

And so, it was. Life was good. I had my family, my friends, and a perfect job; a new outlook on life.

Again, I was getting complimented at work. Staff and costumers regularly remarked on my good looks and appearance, and my slim figure. All in all, I felt good about myself and liked what I saw when I looked in the mirror. I finally saw myself as the outside world saw me. I felt like I had gone from rags to riches overnight on the inside.

Naturally, this new found confidence gave my non-existent ego a massive boost. Very soon, I found myself feeling bored with my mundane life outside work. Discontentment and yearning began to stir in me once again. I thought I had banished those feelings a long time ago.

This change in me was too much too soon for my personality. The ego took over. Ordinary nights sitting at home watching TV became boring and frustrating. I tried not to show this, but my husband did notice a difference in me.

'Will we go out tonight?' I would blurt out of the blue.

'But it's a Thursday night, a school night. Why do you want to go out?'

'I don't know,' I would mumble. 'Just a bit bored.'

I didn't understand then why this discontentment suddenly erupted in me and had many sleepless nights feeling sorry for myself, thinking my life was so dull.

I'm fully aware now why I was feeling that way. When I was young, my fears had always kept me secluded and withdrawn inside. Now, with this new confidence I had acquired, my fears have evaporated. I wanted to be out in the world, to be seen, and heard.

I used to hide from society because I did not have the skills to feel part of it. I had them now, and I wanted to flaunt them everywhere, like the bird freed from the cage, but it was an illusion.

Nevertheless, my ego had risen to such a great extent that I began to resent my role in life, feeling unappreciated and overlooked. This new me was poisonous to my mental state. Unfortunately, I did not have the skills to stop feeding these thoughts. They boiled and boiled, taking away my peace of mind.

I needed a solution so I turned to the one that I'd found all those years ago at the roller disco: alcohol.

We drank socially at weekends with our friends. I loved the drinking Mary still. The confident chatty Mary. I loved letting her out to play. Our drinking was restricted to weekends because of school and work responsibilities. We never indulged midweek, so when I found myself alone in my kitchen on a midweek night with glass in hand, I knew something was changing in me. Unfortunately, I chose to ignore the red flag. That midweek drink was to take me to a depth of despair and self-destruction that I can only describe as hell.

As the midweek drinking night progressed to two or three nights, I began to suffer mild panic attacks. I also started to feel jittery in the mornings. One of these particular anxiety episodes resulted in me taking some time off work. I visited my GP for medication. She was curious about why I would be experiencing these attacks of anxiety.

'Has anything happened lately, Mary?' she inquired of me.

'No, Doctor,' I replied. 'I'm just not sleeping very well.' I did not mention my increasing alcohol intake to her. In truth, I didn't want to admit to myself that it was becoming a problem because I didn't see my drinking as a problem. If there were any niggling doubts in my mind, I pushed them away. Taking these midweek drinks helped me to forget the discontentment and deep yearnings that plagued me constantly.

In short, I was happy when intoxicated. Everything was okay. I was content again, and I could sleep like a baby. Therefore, I was not going to allow any verbal warnings from my GP about the dangers of too much alcohol consumption burst my pink cloud.

Chapter 4

It was Halloween night 2009. I was forty-three then, and we had the usual celebrations. My family, our friends, and their kids would gather together in the big green outside our homes and have a fireworks display. We all loved Halloween, all except our youngest son Danny boy. He was very frightened of the fireworks. My husband or I would have to stay inside with him and look out the window at the displays. He loved watching them explode in the sky, but only if he was inside safe.

I was still drinking excessively, but I managed to keep it under control. I found myself constantly looking forward to my next drink. Danny was nearly eight, and almost as tall as his brother Liam who was ten. My eldest son, Ryan, was now fourteen.

Our sons were three bright, beautiful boys. Ryan, our eldest, was the quietest of the three, a confident teenager. He had his dad's nature. He happily went with the flow of daily life contentedly with no argument. He never craved attention and avoided drama of any kind.

All three of our boys played soccer for local clubs. Liam and Danny also played Gaelic football. Our middle son Liam was outgoing, very independent and mature for his young age. He'd stand his ground when he'd feel things were not going the way he would like them to and he, more so than the other boys, had a real passion for football and soccer.

Our youngest boy Danny was the giddy one. He loved to make us all laugh. He had an infectious giggle and loved to impress. He was very popular in our street and enjoyed playing with his friends. He cherished them and would spend all afternoon on a nice day outside playing rounders or soccer. His friends loved being in his company. Even at the young age of seven, nearly eight, he had an attractive charisma. He also had a sensitive side, which I noticed. I see a lot of myself in my youngest boy.

Our boys were close and helpful to each other. We all had a lot of fun that Halloween evening and, of course, we parents sat in the kitchen and unwound with a few drinks after our duty to the children was over. My favourite part of the night!

The next morning, as I was making breakfast not feeling too good, my two eldest came into the kitchen. A short time later, I noticed that Danny hadn't come down yet. This was unusual as he was always first awake.

'Is Danny boy still asleep?'

'No, Mam. He was awake before us,' they answered.

I went straight upstairs to his room. He was sitting up in bed, holding his stomach when I arrived.

'Danny, are you okay?'

'No, Mam,' he whimpered. 'My belly is sore. I feel sick.'

I hugged him. 'Aw, Son. It's too many sweets and chocolate you had last night. Do you feel like you want to vomit?'

'I think so,' he replied

'Come into the bathroom. I'll stay with you. You will feel better after it comes out.' He didn't really feel much better afterwards and was sick frequently that day and very nauseous. It finally passed away towards evening. I wasn't too concerned, thinking that it was due to the excessive treats the day before.

Danny was still feeling unwell for the rest of the week and was nauseous every morning, some mornings vomiting, and then later in the day, it would pass again. I thought this was very odd and I began to worry. I had to keep him home from school. I postponed returning back to work and took him to see our GP.

She did all the usual tests on Danny's vitals and sent his bloods to be checked. She thought maybe he had developed an allergy to certain foods, and advised me to give him ambrosia rice for a couple of days and bring him back if the vomiting persists. We did as she suggested, but the nausea and vomiting continued. Danny also began to suffer from severe cramping at the back of his knees; this only seemed to occur at night while he was sleeping. He would come into my bedroom whimpering and rubbing his legs. I would take him into my bed and gently rub his legs until he fell back to sleep.

I brought him back to our GP, telling her about his knee cramps. Again, she felt perhaps it was due to his growth spurt and his football and sports. His bloods were fine, so she gave me medication for his nausea and told me to bring him back in a couple of weeks' time if he got no relief. This seemed to work. Danny's vomiting subsided for several days. Although I was concerned. He seemed to be losing weight and looked sickly.

On the Saturday of that week on his medication, Danny had a football match with his team. I was worried. I felt he was too unwell to play.

'Mam, I'm okay. I want to play,' he cried.

I relented.

My husband reassured me that if he felt sick, he would take him straight home.

When they left, I couldn't shake off the feeling of impending doom that had come upon me regarding these strange symptoms my son was showing. I was worried. We both were. I was on tenterhooks until they returned home.

I greeted him when he came through the door. 'Hello, Son. How did the game go?'

'We lost,' he replied downheartedly and ran up to his room.

I looked at my husband. 'Is he okay?'

He had a worried look on his face. 'Mary, the team lost. Danny was in goals, and he could not see the balls coming into the net.'

'What?' I was frantic. 'Sweet Jesus, what is happening to our child?' I said. I began to panic. I went to Danny's room and sat beside him as he was concentrating on a match on the PlayStation. 'Danny, son,' I said. 'Can you pause your game for a minute?'

Putting the pad down, he looked up at me. 'What, Mam?'

'How are you feeling, son?'

'I'm okay.'

'Dad said you didn't see the balls coming into the goals.'

'No, Mam. I didn't.'

'That's okay, son. Can you see alright now?'

'Yeah, I'm fine now, Mam,' he said as he reached for his pad again to continue his challenge match.

He looked up at me again, and for a split second as he stared at me, his eyes turned completely bloodshot, then as quick as it happened, they turned white again.

I stared at him, frozen in shock and bewilderment.

'Mam. Mam!'

I shook my head. 'Sorry, Son. Danny,' I put my arm around him, 'Are you sure you feel okay?'

'Yeah, Mam.' He was getting annoyed at me now for keeping him from his game. 'My head went fuzzy for a while at the match, but I'm okay now. Can I play my game now, Mam?'

'Okay, Son. '

I kissed him and ran down to the kitchen to my husband.

'Something is seriously wrong with Danny,' I blurted out. I sat down and told my husband what happened to Danny's eyes. My heart was racing.

'Sit down and calm down, Mary,' he urged.

I got my breathing under control. We decided I would take Danny to the optician to have his eyes checked. That afternoon, Danny sat in the optician's chair and passed every eye test. He enjoyed the challenge of getting the letters right.

I explained what had happened to his eyes in front of me. She looked a little baffled, so she did an X-ray to check the back of his eyes for clots.

'No,' she informed me. 'His vessels are clear, and his eyesight is perfect.'

I thanked her and left with my son, feeling deflated and even more worried than I had been before she checked him.

I was polishing off the full bottle of wine then. Used to be I would only have a few glasses. That didn't do the trick anymore; that was the progression. My husband didn't remark about my excessive drinking, although I know he wanted to.

I always came up with an excuse for it before he could question me. 'Oh, I just need a few glasses to help me sleep. I'm only having two.'

He would only shrug and leave me to it. Right then, his concerns were with our son Danny, and neither of us wanted to voice our fears to each other. I too was extremely concerned for my child. The difference was, I hid mine in a bottle.

A dark cloud hung around me constantly. A knowing gut feeling that the symptoms my son was having lately were leading to something very sinister and serious.

As soon as these feelings came over me, I would shiver and try to shake them out of my mind or drink them away as I was doing then. In hindsight, I can humble myself now and say that I used this time of worry to justify my drinking. It was all about me.

My friend called to see me one evening, and I sat melancholy and quiet. She knew Danny was unwell and off school. All my family and friends had been asking how he was. She sensed I was not myself and asked me what was wrong.

'There is something badly wrong with Danny boy, Sarah.' The words came out from me with no thought.

'How do you know, Mary?' she replied, shocked.

I looked at her calmly and replied, 'Because I'm his mother!'

On Friday night of that week, Danny started to dry wretch again. Then the vomiting began during the night. It was heart-wrenching to look at him going through this. I felt useless. He never complained or cried. He just did not have a pain that he could point to, which frightened me even more. The heaving finally subsided, and he settled down to sleep.

On Saturday morning around ten, I went to check on him. He was still sleeping, so I left him. He had been through a lot, so I thought the rest would help him, but by twelve, I knew he should be awake. He would never sleep this late. He was only barely eight years old.

I shook him gently to stir him awake. He opened his eyes slowly. Again, I noticed how pale and thin he was becoming.

'Danny, it's twelve o'clock,' I said. 'Do you not want to get up, son?'

'No, Mam,' he croaked. 'I'm too tired.'

'Okay, I'll bring you up a juice. I'll be back in a wee minute.'

I had to leave the room as fast as I could. I felt the tears welling in my eyes as he looked at me — such a sickly look on his beautiful face. I ran down the stairs and lifted the phone to my husband.

'Dessie,' I cried down the phone. 'Danny can't stay awake. I can't let him go through any more. I am taking him to the emergency GP to get a letter for the hospital.'

'Okay, Mary, I'll come with you. I'll be home as soon as I can.'

My husband arrived home. We quickly bundled Danny into the car, quietly telling him that the doctor wanted to see how he was doing now. I held him in my arms. He was quiet and lethargic.

As we sat in the doctor's office, I began to tell him all about Danny's symptoms, and when they started. My son was sitting on my knee.

'Okay,' the doctor sighed. After he had written down what I told him, he turned to Danny. 'Danny,' he said calmly. 'I would like you to do a few easy exercises for me now if you can.'

My sweet son smiled and nodded at the doctor in reply. Danny had a smile that would light up a room, and I smiled to see it.

'Will you stand in front of me, Danny, please?'

Danny moved straight away to get off my knee in obedience. As he stood in front of the doctor, the doctor asked Danny to cover one of his eyes.

'Can you see me with the other eye?' he asked my son.

'Yes', Danny boy said with a nod.

The doctor then told him to do the same with the opposite eye. 'And can you see me now?'

'Yes,' my son replied.

The doctor then placed his hands horizontally each side of Danny's head and said, 'I'd like you to tell me if you can see my fingers, just by turning your eyes.'

My son stalled for a moment. I could see his face changing. I knew he couldn't see. I sucked in a sob.

'I only see shadows,' Danny replied. He was so weak and trying so hard to please the doctor.

'That's fine, Danny,' the doctor continued. 'Now, I want you to walk in a straight line, one foot in front of the other. '

My husband and I looked at each other in total confusion. Why was the doctor asking our son to perform these tasks? But we sat in silence because this doctor was our only hope now to find out what was wrong with our child.

Danny did as the doctor asked slowly but quite well.

'Very good, Danny,' he boosted him. 'Now, I want you to stand on one leg for me if you can.' I looked at my son's face, the determination. He was a bit wobbly on this exercise, but he maintained the stance for as long as he could. He stood there in only his pyjamas, pale and thin, clearly feeling very ill. Yet, he was pushing himself to his limits because the doctor asked him to.

He had to do the same exercise with his other leg, then again, he wobbled. I saw the disappointment in his eyes, I whispered over to him, 'It's okay, Son, if you are a bit wobbly. You still pass the test.' I had to say something to encourage him.

When the exercise was completed, the doctor turned to my husband. 'Would you take Danny out to the waiting room for a few minutes, please? I'd like to talk to his mother for a moment.'

We all sat in silence for a moment looking from one to another. The doctor began to write as my husband then picked Danny up in his arms and took him outside. 'Mrs McFadden, I have written a letter for you to give to the desk at the hospital.' He stopped talking and sighed. Then he looked at me straight in the eyes. My heart was thumping like a drum. 'I want Danny to be checked for a brain tumour.'

Time stopped. What I experienced at that moment hearing this news can only be described as an electric shock through my body. My head went light, and I had a ringing sensation in my ears, then numbness, nothing, an out of body experience. I put my hand across the table to take the letter from him, the doctor was saying something to me, but his words were muffled to my ears like I was underwater.

He repeated my name. I shook my head in an attempt to hear his words.

'Mrs McFadden, don't be worrying unnecessarily right now,' he said. 'This is only a process of elimination. It could be simply a virus he has contracted. Keep positive.'

I merely nodded. The words brain tumour were resounding around my head.

I told my husband outside the car when we had Danny settled in the back seat, what the doctor had said.

'What!' my husband said shocked. 'A brain tumour? Why would he want him checked for that?'

'He just wants to eliminate the possibility. He said not to worry,' I replied.

Of course, we were worried. While we sat in the cubicle in the accident and emergency department of the hospital, waiting for a doctor to examine Danny, I was still in that detached state unable to completely absorb what was going on around me. Danny seemed to be getting weaker in front of our eyes and slipped in and out of small naps.

We tried to keep his spirits up by making jokes and laughing. Around half an hour later, a couple of doctors came in. They began to check Danny's vitals, all the while asking us questions about his symptoms and how long he had been ill. After explaining, they left, then a short time later, more doctors did the same and left.

This went on for a couple of hours, and eventually, I asked my husband if he would go back home to the boys. It was getting late, and my sons at home needed one of us to be there. This was very upsetting for them also, not knowing what was happening to their brother. I reassured him that I would phone as soon as I knew anything.

It was late into the night, and Danny was sleeping. I was trying to concentrate on a magazine article I was reading when a nurse popped into the cubicle. 'Mrs McFadden, we are going to take Danny down now for a brain scan.'

'Okay,' I said. 'Can I wake him for you?'

'Of course, I'll be back in a few minutes.'

I walked alongside my son's trolley bed on the way to X-ray, holding his hand and reassuring him that he would be okay. He was too weak to put up any resistance anyway. When we were back in the cubicle after Danny's X-ray, I was chatting with my son about Christmas. It was now the 6th of December and Danny had been telling his dad and I that he wanted a new PlayStation from Santa this year. A nurse put her head into the cubicle and asked if she could speak to me outside for a moment — another electric shock shot through my body.

'Mrs McFadden,' she spoke slowly in a very soft voice. 'The scan we took of Danny's brain is showing an abnormality. We are not sure what is going on. There is swelling.'

My heart began to pound in my chest. My head went light. I could not respond to her. She put her arm around my shoulder.

'Try not to worry. We are going to send him to Beaumont by ambulance when one becomes available. In the meantime, we will admit him to the children's ward tonight.'

I tried to gather myself. Shrugging her arm from me, I mumbled, 'When you say an abnormality on his brain, what does that mean? Like, is there something there that should not be there?' I was whimpering.

'We can't see anything conclusive,' she replied. 'The swelling is preventing a clear picture of his brain. The doctors in Beaumont have specialists in this area.'

I merely nodded in response. 'Can you stay with my son for a few minutes until I phone my husband, please?' I asked.

'Of course,' she replied politely.

I went to my son. 'Danny, I'm just going to get a coffee. I'll bring you a juice back. Okay, Son?'

'Okay, Mam.'

I left, nearly running to the door. I needed air. I felt the walls closing in on me.

My husband was silent on the phone when I told him.

'Okay, stay calm, Mary. I'm on my way up to you.'His voice was shaky.

When I hung up, I was almost afraid to cry. I was afraid of what would erupt in me if I let go. Instead, I worked on my breathing to regulate my racing heart and went back to my son.

A week later, Danny was still in hospital with no diagnosis yet. This was 13 December 2009. The doctors had done several scans and X-rays on my son and taken blood tests daily with no conclusive results. He was pale and lethargic but alert and chatty. His nausea had subsided. He was on a drip for nutrients and eating small amounts, mainly yoghurts, and some toast. The doctors thought he might have contracted a virus of some description. Danny was a champion patient. All the nurses loved him. He had a smile for everyone. Never cried or complained despite the constant blood tests and poking he received daily.

My husband and I were rotating shifts to be with him all the time. My brother and niece had practically moved into our home to be there for our sons at home, keeping their daily routine as normal as possible. All my family and friends had rallied around for us being tremendously helpful and supportive. For me, though, time stood still. Life did not exist outside those walls then, and I lived each day fighting against a knowing instinctive feeling of doom stirring inside me.

One morning into the second week of Danny's stay, one of the doctors asked my husband and I to come to his office for a chat.

My oldest sister Lizzy and her husband Mike were with us in the ward. They had come to visit Danny. They chatted with our son while we went to the doctor's office.

We sat tense and silent across from his desk.

'We have scrutinised Danny's brain scans,' he said. 'And we can see no evidence of a brain tumour.' He had to stop talking, as we both broke down and cried with relief. It felt like we had only started breathing again since the 6th of December.

I composed myself and looked at the doctor. By his expression, he did not seem to share in our joy. So if there is no brain tumour, doctor, then what is wrong with Danny?' I asked quietly, almost afraid of his reply.

'Honestly, we don't know.'

Our momentary happiness dissipated.

'Your son has a lot of swelling at the back of his brain. Until this is relieved, we cannot get a proper picture of what's going on. We need to do a procedure known as a shunt. We insert a tube into the back of his brain to drain the fluid off. Then we will do more scans and hopefully pinpoint what is occurring.'

I was trying to absorb this news when my husband said, 'Doctor, is there any chance Danny will be home for Christmas?'

'I cannot say for certain but if this is successful and we diagnose a virus, get the antiviral to eliminate it, then it's possible, yes. But don't get your hopes up yet.'

We left the office, both relieved and still worried. My husband stayed that night. Danny was going down early in the morning for his procedure. On the train home, I sat with tears rolling down my cheeks at the memory of my child's smile as I'd left him. He'd looked so sick, yet he'd hugged me and made me promise to bring him up the hardest jigsaw puzzle I could find for him to challenge himself.

'Not one of those baby ones, Mam,' he'd implored. 'Get me a very hard one. '

My beautiful son. He humbled me beyond words.

I reflected back to my stay in hospital when I was about his age. I'd cry every night for my mammy, and made the nurses' lives hell — not my Danny boy, smiling all the way.

I turned my thoughts to my sons at home. They too had shown such maturity. Never complaining or making demands. My eldest was only fifteen; my middle son barely eleven. I made a firm resolution then to spend some quality time with them when I got home.

We had decided not to mention the procedure to them. Why worry them? My thoughts were interrupted by the waiter on the train.

'Would you like anything from the bar?'

'Yes,' I replied after a moment. 'I'll have a glass of white wine, please.'

It frightened me how quickly I drank that wine, plus two more. Even more concerning was the way it immediately eradicated my tension.

My sons and I spent a nice evening together, watching a movie. I reassured them that Danny was okay and still having tests done. I told them they could go up in a couple of days. That made them happy. They missed their young brother. It broke my heart to see the concern in their eyes.

Mid-morning the next day, my husband phoned to tell me Danny's procedure was over and that it went very well. I was relieved. My husband sounded the same. On the train journey back up to the hospital an hour later, I began to wonder should I dare hope that Danny would be better soon? That we could have him home for Christmas?

By the time I got to the hospital, I was very anxious to see my son. My husband greeted me.

'Mary, everything went well. Danny is still groggy from the anaesthetic.'

I went to my son's bedside. He had tubes in his nose and one at the back of his head draining the fluid. His hair was shaven off at the side of his head, and monitors bleeped all around him. I took his fragile, bruised hand in mine and rubbed it. Tears welled up in my eyes. He looked so sick and weak. I composed myself and turned to my husband.

'You go on home now,' I urged him. 'You look exhausted. I'm here now, and I'll phone you when Danny wakes up. You need rest.'

He agreed. We hugged. He kissed our son and left.

After a while of watching my child, waiting for him to recover from his antistatic, I reached over and whispered in his ear, 'Mam's here, Son. You're okay.'

Suddenly, his hand twitched in mine. I stood back to stare at his face. Within a moment, his whole body began to twitch and then began to shake violently.

I screamed for the nurse.

Within minutes, there were doctors and nurses surrounding his bed and pulling the curtain around. One of the nurses was trying to usher me away, but I was frantic. I pulled away and yanked the curtain across to see my child. I stood motionless when I saw my child convulsing in the bed. Blood trickled down his nostrils. I couldn't move.

I felt my arm being tugged. The nurse finally got me away to the station, where I sat totally stunned beyond words. I was frozen in shock. The nurses were saying something to me. I couldn't hear anything except the drum of my heartbeat in my chest.

I looked up then to see the surgeon standing in front of me. I stared at him for what seemed an eternity. I heard myself mumble, 'What happened, Doctor?'

I noticed he looked shaken. 'Your son's had a seizure. '

'But why?' I cried.

Frustrated, he replied, 'I don't know. '

I began to wail uncontrollably. There were no more words to be said right then. A while later, the doctor came to me as I sat in the hall, in oblivion.

'Danny has recovered,' he said. 'You can go to him now, but I need to tell you that he has not regained his speech yet. Please, don't panic about this,' he urged me. 'It is common after a seizure. His voice should return soon.'

'Should,' I replied, numb with shock.

The doctor simply nodded. 'Mrs McFadden,' he continued. 'We have the top neurosurgeons on Danny's case. We will get to the cause and treat your son accordingly.'

I sighed. 'I know, Doctor. Thank you. I do appreciate everything you are doing for my son.'

I got up from my chair and went to my child.

Danny lay there, staring into space. I took his hand in mine. He turned his gaze to my face. His beautiful sky-blue eyes looked empty. I could feel a lump rising in my throat.

'Hello, Son,' I said quietly as I kissed him on his forehead. I was holding back tears as I began to explain to my son why he could not speak. I told him that his voice was in shock right now because of the test on his head and that his voice would return soon.

'Don't be afraid, Danny boy. You will be better soon. Everything is going to be okay.' I filled him with empty promises. He simply stared at me unresponsive and clearly bewildered and confused.

A nurse who was nearby overheard me talking and came to the bedside.

'Danny,' she said brightly. 'Why don't we see if you can answer by blinking your eyes? If the answer is "yes", blink once, and if it's "no" blink twice. Let's try this,' she said as she turned to me for approval.

I merely nodded. Her timing was perfect. At that point where she'd intervened, I had truly been at the end of my rope emotionally. I'd been holding back a flood of tears and despair. I'd never felt so useless as a mother.

'Let's start then,' the nurse continued. 'Are you thirsty, Danny?'

I was fixated on my child's face in anticipation for his response.

He blinked once.

I let out a sigh of relief, lifting his cup with the straw to his mouth. Then I noticed how shaky his limp hands were as he tried to hold the cup.

'Very good, Danny,' the nurse said. 'Now Mum, you ask a question.'

'Okay,' I tried to sound cheerful. 'Danny, do you like carrots?'

My son grinned very slightly then blinked twice for no. I giggled at him. We continued communicating like this for a little while.

Danny began to tire. His eyes were sleepy.

'Have a wee nap, Son.' I urged him. 'I'll be here when you wake up.'

He closed his eyes.

I kissed him and left to phone my husband. When I had finished telling him, he was silent. I could imagine his face at home at getting the news.

He was shocked and distraught as I expected, although he kept his voice calm for my sake. We agreed not to tell the boys at home yet.

On my way back to Danny's ward, one of the doctors on Danny's case stopped me and asked to speak with me.

'We have decided to send Danny to Temple Street Hospital tomorrow to have a biopsy done,' he said.

I froze on the spot.

'But why do you need a biopsy done?' I quizzed.

'We haven't detected a virus yet. We feel that since the swelling has gone down, it's wise to do a biopsy even though there is nothing conclusive on the scans to detect a tumour,' he said.

I simply stared into space. I had no reply. I put my head in my hands. There was no fight left in me.

I sighed. 'You know what's best, Doctor. Go ahead with your plans. I need to be with my child now if that's okay?'

The doctor nodded to me, sympathetically.

A while later as I sat in the canteen in the hospital while Danny was sleeping again, I phoned my husband to tell him of the latest plans for Danny. Again, he tried to keep his emotions under control for me by being positive. I knew he was crumbling inside. Unfortunately, I had no empathy for his feelings at that time. I was empty inside and full of self-pity.

After our chat, I suddenly got an overwhelming urge to get out of the hospital. I felt the walls were closing in on me. Out of nowhere, a thought came to me. There's a bar on the corner, and before I could analyse what I was doing, I was walking to the pub. The air was icy cold. I hadn't noticed it really until then.

The lounge was warm and cosy; it was low lit with comfortable large armchairs. There were only a few customers scattered around. I found a secluded corner and sat down. The television was showing the weather forecast for the coming weeks. I could hear the voices of a couple of customers grumbling at the bar about snow. My child's face came to my mind – laughing as he threw snowballs at us. As I began to question why I was there, a waiter came to ask me if I would like a drink.

My doubts vanished. 'I'll have a pint of Guinness, please,' I said.

As I sat there in that lounge, I forcefully pushed all emotions away. I felt solace and escapism. Even though logic told me I couldn't escape this, alcohol told me a different story, and I chose to believe the fairy-tale for that short time. It seemed to me that this was not a conscious decision from an intelligent mind, but rather it had simply happened and here I was. I know now that it was not intellect that placed me there; rather, it was my progressing diseased alcoholic thinking that once again won me over.

I had three pints of Guinness, and, as always, it provided just what it always did for me, which was serenity and a calm mind. It was my solution, except this time I used it for a different reason. Since my early teens, alcohol had helped me to feel part of society, gave me confidence, and helped me to communicate with the outside world with no underlying fears. This time, I needed it to help me not to feel at all. As usual, I got what I wanted.

However, this numbness I yearned for was to be short-lived. When I arrived back to my son's bedside and sat there looking at his beautiful face, pale and thin as he slept, as the monitors bleeped all around him, my mind was flooded with guilt, shame, and remorse. I hated myself. I kissed him as tears of guilt and disgust at myself rolled from my eyes.

The next morning my son was a little brighter, although he still could not speak, he seemed chirpier and smiled more as we communicated.

My husband arrived, and I knew in an instant that he had not slept well. His eyes looked swollen, and his face gaunt. I felt a pang of sympathy for him. As he got settled in beside Danny, he began asking the yes-no questions as I had informed him to do.

He was nervous and tried his best to keep it hidden from our child. Guilt hit me once again as I watched them together, remembering my behaviour last night. As I kissed my son goodbye telling him I would be up later to see him, my husband walked out with me. We hugged, and he tried as always to keep positive. I could not seem to get myself in that frame of mind. Perhaps I was afraid to.

We had explained to Danny that he would be having another test done. This was hard as I knew he was afraid, yet he could not tell us. We discussed it as briefly as possible for him and went on to talk of more cheerful things to take this mind off of it. My husband had brought a new movie for him to watch on his portable DVD. This helped him to forget about what lay ahead.

As I sat on the train home, I was almost relieved to be away from the hospital. This was the first time I felt this way leaving Danny. Perhaps, looking at him helplessly as he lay in that hospital bed ill and weak, unable to communicate with anyone, was beginning to break me. The never-ending blood tests he endured, the monitors, the sick children everywhere with parents huddled around them anxious and worried, and my poor son lying in the middle of this, sick and silent. I can only describe it as watching the saddest movie you've ever seen and being unable to switch the TV off. Your child is the star of the show.

Put simply, I felt useless. This filled me with frustration and, of course, self-pity – my biggest defect. I turned my thoughts to my older sons at home. My husband and I had decided that we would tell them Danny could not speak right now. I was going to deliver the news to them tonight. The reservations I had about it could also have been a factor in my unusual urgency to get out of the hospital. In any case, I needed to focus on them now. They were both vulnerable, both confused and scared; yet I had no answers for them.

We sat on the bed that night, my sons and I. I put my arms around them, and I began to explain. My voice was shaky. I was so afraid of their reaction to this awful news. I feared that if they cried, I would fall apart.

My worries were unfounded. As usual, they took the news well. They humbled me yet again by the strength and maturity they displayed, even though I knew as their mother that both of them were extremely anxious and worried for their brother. I could tell by the look in their eyes, and the concern in their faces.

I reassured them that Danny would get his voice back. That he was fine otherwise, watching his movies and enjoying the attention. None of that was true. I had to lie for their sake at that time.

Later that night, my mother phoned. I was receiving so many calls from concerned family members and friends. I mostly only sent multiple texts to everyone, keeping them updated. Sometimes, I didn't even have the motivation to do that. My husband did most of it for us. It's hard to explain why I was in that frame of mind. Certainly, I appreciated everybody for their support. Unfortunately, I simply couldn't find the mental energy to talk to anybody really. Perhaps I was afraid because to talk about Danny being so ill made it a reality.

But where my mother was concerned, I had to talk to her. She was so worried. Knowing her as well as I did, I was very aware of how distraught she was. After a brief conversation with her where I explained about the biopsy, she wished me goodnight, telling me we were all in her prayers.

'Danny is a strong wee man, Mags,' she said then.

My mother called me Mags as a pet name sometimes, usually when she knew I was in distress. During that period of time, I always breathed a sigh of relief when I hung up from my conversations with Mam. Not because she was demanding or interfering, it was rather because I was trying to hold back my tears. I wanted to scream, cry, and wail to my mother. I wanted to tell her how afraid I was, how I truly felt that Danny was very seriously ill, how heart-wrenching it was to see him like this, to know what he was enduring, how confused and scared my boys at home were, not knowing the right way to approach them, or what to say. We don't get a guide book as parents for such traumatic times as this.

I refrained time and again to let go to my mother. I'm not really sure why but the underlying reason was that I would feel so guilty breaking down like that to Mam. To only hang up and leave her crying with worry for me.

That vision of my mother's tears alone at home would undoubtedly put me over the edge. Ultimately, owing to this frame of mind I was in, it put a wedge between her and me. I had to try to sound strong for her sake, and she was talking positively to me for mine. It led to strained conversations as we tiptoed around each other with our words. It left me emotionally starved. I'm sure my poor mam felt the same.

It was the 23rd of December, and as I sat in our home looking around at all the effort my family and friends had gone to make our house look festive for the boys at home, I felt humbled and grateful. My brother had even decorated the garden with Santas and lights. We were truly blessed to have so many people in our lives who love us. For some reason, I felt undeserving of this outpouring of unconditional love. I was pondering on this when my husband came through the back door followed by his brother Martin who also looked shaken.

I froze. 'Dessie, why are you here?'

He was silent for a moment. He came to me. 'Mary, sit down for a minute, please.'

'What is it?' I screeched.

He guided me to the sofa and sat beside me. Martin sat opposite at the kitchen table.

'Mary, Danny is still in recovery from the biopsy. The doctor came to see me. They did a scan before the procedure. They found a tumour, Mary, at the stem of Danny's brain.'

I couldn't respond except to shake my head from side to side, wishing I did not have to hear it. I put my head in my hands and rocked back and forth. I mumbled to my husband, 'Is the tumour cancerous?'

He whimpered back, 'Yes.' He reached for my hand, and I pulled away.

My brother-in-law went to our boys upstairs to keep them amused.

The strange thing here is that I had no obvious emotional response at getting this horrendous news. I went into shock, I suppose. My mind could not absorb it. My husband cried silently beside me, yet this didn't move me at all.

I became a lone wolf once more. The shield went up. These behaviours were my coping skills. They were the only ones I knew how to work with. My poor husband was ashen white in despair and worried sick for his son's life.

I simply turned to autopilot just to stop myself from breaking down entirely. Feeling completely detached, I turned to my husband

'I'm going up now, Dessie,' I said bluntly. 'I have to be there when Danny returns from theatre.'

My husband lifted his slumped head and looked at me. Wiping his eyes, he took a deep breath. 'I'm going with you,' he said.

We went to the boys and told them that we had to go up to hear about Danny's test results. We would phone them in a while.

My brother-in-law stayed with them.

Danny had arrived back to the ward just before we arrived. We went to his bedside. He was still groggy from the anaesthetic. He had a bandage at the side of his head, and his hair was shaven around the area. To me, my child looked more sickly and thin than he had the previous day. The tears came then. They rolled down my cheeks as I tried hard to weep silently so as not to frighten him. Putting my arms gently around him, I kissed him on the forehead and told him I loved him and was so proud of him. His eyes fluttered. My husband sat opposite me holding his hand. We sat like that silently for several minutes.

A doctor arrived and asked to speak with us for a few minutes. We followed him to the nurses' station.

'Mr and Mrs McFadden, we will be sending Danny back to Temple Street Children's Hospital. They have the specialists for treating Danny there. I can only imagine how shocked you both are but be assured the doctors there will do their very best to treat your son.'

'Doctor,' I whimpered. 'Is my son in any pain lying there?'

'Absolutely not,' he answered sympathetically. 'We have him on a high dose of pain relief, which is monitored and given regularly through IV. This will, of course, make him very groggy and a bit disorientated, so he will sleep a lot. '

'When is he being moved?' my husband inquired.

'Tomorrow morning,' the doctor replied.

We thanked him and returned to our son.

A while later Danny began to come around fully. We chatted with him but kept it simple because he could only blink his response to us. The first thing I noticed was that his pupils seemed to be very dilated and he was fidgety. I brought his cup with the straw to his mouth and gave him several drinks.

He was thirsty and extremely weak. He was hardly able to lift his arm, and when he did try, his hands shook nervously. This frightened me. He seemed to be losing all his strength and coordination at an extremely fast rate, although I didn't word these concerns to my husband.

As we sat with him, kissing his face and talking cheerily with him, he seemed to gaze at us rather than look, like he couldn't really see us. Perhaps this was because of his high dose of medication, but that inner gut instinct that plagued me with dread was upon me again. My son was a shell of that bright, giddy, smiling, big, happy boy he had been only a few weeks ago.

Urging my husband to go home then for some much-needed rest, I stayed with Danny boy that night.

The next morning, I travelled with Danny in the ambulance to Temple Street Children's Hospital, which was only a short ten minute or so distance. As I climbed out of the ambulance and waited at the entrance for them to take Danny from the ambulance, I noticed again just how cold it was. Flutters of snow fell. It made me sad and melancholy. This was Danny boy's favourite season. I had to shake myself to regain my composure.

Later, after Danny was settled in, I was leaving the ward to phone my husband. In the corridor, I was stopped by a nurse. Before she spoke to me, there were suddenly several doctors around me, including the neurosurgeon.

One of the doctors spoke to me. 'There is nothing to be alarmed about, Mrs McFadden. We just want to tell you that we will need to see both of you early this evening for a meeting regarding treatment for Danny. We would have liked to do this earlier, but unfortunately, one of our specialists is held up until later.'

I stood speechless as I looked from one doctor to another. What happened to me then can only be described as a breakdown. Something snapped in my mind, bringing up a surge of anger. All the traumatic events that had turned our lives upside down in the last month or so seemed to land on my head right then and there. It was the straw that broke the camels back for me.

My husband and I had timed our day so that he could do all he needed to do, in preparation for Christmas day for the boys, and then get up to the hospital in time for me to catch the train home. It was Christmas Eve, and the last train was leaving Dublin earlier than usual. Now that plan would have to be rearranged, and although it seemed trivial, in that scenario then, and given my mental and emotional state, I exploded.

'Don't you doctors realise that we have two sons at home, a ten-year-old and a fifteen-year-old? This is Christmas Eve. My eight-year-old son is lying in that bed, dying before my eyes.'

My voice trembled as I said these words. I raged on

'I'm phoning my husband to come up so that I can get an early train home to try to make some kind of a half-decent Christmas for my boys at home.'

The doctors simply stared at me silently. A nurse tried to calm me down to no avail. I was out of control.

'My child is a shell of the perfect, beautiful boy he was a month ago and we are worried sick. He can't even feed himself,' I began to wail. 'You all stand here telling me what you need me to do to suit your arrangements.'

Again, the nurse came to me to try to calm me down.

'Leave me alone,' I roared. I turned away from them and left the ward, leaving astounded silence behind me.

Later in the day, my husband and I sat side by side motionless and silent in a large bright room. I had purposely focused my mind to a shiny mahogany table at which we were seated. I could tell it had been recently polished because the aroma of furniture polish still clung to the air.

A nurse sat next to my husband. The neurosurgeon sat opposite us with her assistant next to her. I had my guard up. I told myself that no matter what news we were given, I must stay focused on what the doctor was telling us. To do this, I had to switch my emotions off for now.

Danny's surgeon introduced herself and her assistant. Clasping both her hands together, she leaned across the table to us and began by explaining the procedures that led to Danny's diagnosis.

'Mr and Mrs McFadden,' she continued in a quiet calm voice. 'Danny has a tumour at the stem of his brain. It has disseminated, which means the tumour has broken up and is spreading through the plasma of his brain. Now, my team and I have been discussing treatments,' she went on.

'Danny will need both radiotherapy and chemotherapy in that sequence. Because the tumour is at the top of his spine, the procedure for treatment is very intricate and delicate. We will have to have a mould made for his head. Accuracy is of utmost importance as the slightest movement of his head during treatment could result in damage to his spinal cord. For this reason, surgery is not an option either. We intend to start treatment on Danny after the New Year. He will require both treatments for the duration of fifteen months, and we will do regular scans during this time to monitor any success. ' She finally stopped talking and sat back in the chair to wait for our reaction.

My eyes had been glued to her face the whole time she was speaking, and yet, I had no reaction. For me, it was like listening to her talk about somebody I didn't know. I think I chose that scenario in my mind because there was no way I could absorb the fact that this was my child she was talking about.

Still silent and motionless, I turned to the sound of my husband sobbing as the nurse next to him consoled him. 'What was wrong with me?' I remember thinking. The only thing I could form in my mind was the words 'mould for his head' and 'damage spinal cord,' after that were the words, 'My child is doomed.'

All I could feel was the erratic beating of my heart and a ringing in my ears.

The surgeon spoke again slowly in a sympathetic voice.

'I know this news is a terrible shock to you both, but I can assure you that we will do everything possible to eliminate this cancer.'

A new sentence popped into my head while she spoke. My child will suffer more. With these thoughts swirling around my mind, I looked the surgeon straight in the eye. 'Doctor,' I croaked. My throat had dried up. 'What is the cure rate for a cancer like Danny's?'

She avoided my stare.

'I can't say for sure, I'm afraid. This is a rare, aggressive cancer. Maybe 70%, 30% but this is only guessing. Every patient is different.'

I searched her face for a glimmer of hope in her answer. I saw none. As if reading my thoughts, my husband, through his tears, said, 'Doctor, is there hope for my son?'

With his words, my eyes finally began to weep.

Pushing her chair back in a motion to leave, the doctor replied in a melancholy voice. 'There is always hope,' she said.

Four more words popped into my mind: 'Not for Danny boy.'

I had subconsciously gone into complete denial when I left the room that day. I found myself comforting my husband, which I hadn't done up to that point. On the train home that Christmas Eve evening, the pain in my chest that I had been carrying since all this began, had lifted and the despair had ebbed away.

For whatever reason, I found myself looking forward to getting home to my other boys. Whatever had occurred in my mind was what I needed right now. On reflection, I realise that this extreme denial was also a coping skill. One that I hadn't used in a long time. I was going to my childhood fantasy land.

My phone rang, making me jump. It was my niece, Lucy. She had been of tremendous help to us. She loves our boys, is our chief babysitter, and has been in their lives since they were babies.

'Hi Mary,' she said cheerily. 'How is Danny now?'

'Things are still the same,' I lied. For whatever reason, I simply did not want to tell her the awful news right now. She was with our boys at home, and I felt I needed to be there to tell her out of earshot from the boys for now.

'Okay,' she said. 'I'm ringing to tell you that I have the boys in town with the rest of the family. I thought it would be a good idea to take them out.'

'Okay,' I said. 'Thanks, Lucy.'

'We won't be that long,' she continued. 'I'll take them for something to eat and then home.'

I thanked her again and hung up.

Every year on Christmas Eve, there was a family meet in town with our kids, and we'd have a wee pre-Christmas drink and something to eat. Although I was grateful to my niece for taking the boys, I hadn't contemplated that they would not be there when I got home. Straight away, my mood started to change. A feeling of loneliness began to embrace me, followed by the familiar despair that had eased momentarily earlier. As I sat back in the seat on the train, my mind went to Danny boy, as I visualised him lying there limp and almost lifeless in the hospital bed. The realisation came to me that I had absolutely no control over what would befall my son in the future. All I could see for him ahead was pain.

Danny was the mammy's boy in our family, always turning to me with whatever ailed him. Like I with my mother, we have like a soul mate connection. He was very much like me at that age in personality. Sometimes I could tell how he was feeling simply by looking into his eyes. This awareness was a curse to me now, knowing the suffering and painful path he was on for the foreseeable future and so ultimately the pink cloud of detachment I had experienced briefly had abruptly burst into a wave of despairing, futile tears.

By the time I got home, there was nothing left inside, only emptiness. As I sat in the kitchen, I was very aware that I was on thin ice regarding my emotional state and feared I would go insane. The lack of control over the future for my son left me feeling inadequate as a mother. All of these thoughts that were coming up were simply twisted forms of self-pity, which thankfully I'm well aware of now.

The house was eerily quiet without my boys here. My first thought was, I don't want to be alone, and because my family had all the Christmas dinner prepared for us for tomorrow and the house decorated, tidy and clean, there was little for me to do now except to wrap our boys' gifts up. This, I was avoiding. Thinking about going through Danny's Christmas presents only added to my depressed state.

I reached for the phone to call my mother but stopped abruptly knowing that I would have to go into the whole episode about Danny's diagnosis. My husband and I had phoned our families and friends earlier to tell them the news of his cancer. We'd made the conversations very brief. It was too hard to talk about it in detail with everyone.

We also decided that we would not tell the boys now. To our minds, as their parents, we saw no point in giving them this frightening news on Christmas Eve. My mother had been calm in her reaction or trying to sound calm. I knew, though, that she was crumbling inside. This was my reasoning for changing my mind about phoning her at that point. To offload my distress on her now would only leave her feeling just like I did. Why burden her anymore? She had to absorb the shock herself.

So, putting the phone down I sat staring into space. I neither wanted to be alone nor have company. My emotions were in turmoil, and I couldn't form a rational thought. To sit there alone in a vulnerable zombie state like that on Christmas Eve was a big mistake because within moments I was out of the chair and opening the fridge for the bottle of wine. The familiar pattern of thinking about drinking when I was afraid, jumped into my mind, and I could feel my body and mind relaxing the minute I took the first sip.

Knowing what I do now, I realise the thought pattern I engaged in on that evening was my alcoholic thinking. I fed into it to justify me taking a drink. I drank the first glass at an alarmingly fast pace. I poured another and only then could I find the false courage to face going up to the attic to take our sons gifts down. I took my bottle with me.

By the time my sons came home, I was tipsy and in full cheer at their arrival. We chatted, and I told them we would all go up tomorrow to Danny with his presents. Later that night, when they were sleeping, I told my niece of the news about Danny's cancer.

She, like everyone else, was shocked and worried but tried to remain positive for my sake. This was the emotional block for me with regard to family and friends. I wanted to voice my despair, my doubts, and my fears that perhaps Danny wouldn't survive but I refrained from doing this. It was partly because I wanted to stay in denial, but the main reason was it simply felt like I would be hurting them, leaving them in a state of despair.

So it was that we walked on eggshells in each other's company emotionally. A noise from downstairs woke me up abruptly. Looking at my clock, it was 5 am. Realising it was Christmas morning left me with a dull ache. I put on my dressing gown and went downstairs. My husband was sitting slumped in the chair in the kitchen, looking forlorn as he sat stroking our collie's head.

We had agreed yesterday that he would come home early to be here with the boys when they opened their presents, and later in the morning, we'd all go up to Danny too and give him his gifts. My husband looked up at me. His eyes were bloodshot and swollen. He looked like he was on the verge of collapse. I was concerned. Sitting across from him at the kitchen table, I asked him if he was okay

'Mary,' he began in a quivering voice. 'I drove down that motorway cursing God. There was no traffic on the motorway, and I never felt so alone in my life. My temper went. All I could think about was Danny lying alone in that bed on Christmas morning. 'He began to whimper.

Tears rolled down my cheeks, listening to his pain.

'I cursed God the whole way home,' he continued. 'I asked him what did I do to deserve this? What did my child do? What kind of God are you anyway?'He bent forward with his head in his hand and cried.

I had no words of wisdom for him, no clichés of positivity. I simply went to him and held him until his tears subsided.

It was the worst Christmas morning imaginable for us as a family as we tried with all our might to look excited for our boys as they tore open their presents under the tree. All that was on my mind was getting back up to the hospital to be with Danny boy. My husband assured me that after explaining to the nurse he would be gone for a while, she had kindly offered to be there if Danny woke up and keep him company until we arrived back. Although our boys at home were delighted with the gifts they received, I couldn't help noticing the sadness in their eyes too. They clearly missed their wee brother there in our home on Christmas morning.

A couple of hours later, we were all in the car on the way to the hospital to be with our Danny boy. I was worried on the journey up. The boys were content playing the consoles in the back of the car. I was concerned for them and Danny's reaction when he saw them. We hadn't mentioned Christmas to Danny recently. It was hard enough for him having to be in hospital away from everyone he loved, sickly and unable to speak but what concerned me more than anything, was the fact that Danny would not be able to speak to his brothers. This was the hardest thing for him, I know, and for them too. I wanted to scream at the injustice to my children.

Danny boy was their baby brother and the life and soul of our home. He was smart and feisty, sporty and kind, with the most infectious giggle. He helped his big brothers in football games when they needed a player. Teamed up with them in two-player games on the PlayStation, and took their orders for the kitchen for treats, which he brought up to them in their rooms. He loved his big brothers, and they loved him.

Unfortunately, the boy lying in the hospital bed was not the Danny boy that played with his brothers a couple of months ago. He was now very ill, thin, and weak. Thankfully, I underestimated my sons.

When we arrived at Danny's bedside, they went to him easily and greeted their brother with a hug. My heart was bursting with pride. They did not ask any questions.

My husband and I improvised in any situation where it was awkward by talking to all three of them together. I did notice that Danny seemed, to my mind, to tense up a bit while his brothers were with him, and I know this was because he wanted to communicate with them, to have fun and be the brother he always was around them. He could not. He was too weak. I looked on while my sons sat with their brother, helping him to open his presents. I had to take a step back. I could feel the tears welling in my eyes. The lump in my throat choking me. The reality of my child's condition hit me hard in the face.

While the majority of families were gathered together around the Christmas tree, mothers focusing on cooking the turkey and preparing the perfect Christmas dinner, for all the parents there in that children's' ward on Christmas day, time stood still. You learn to live in the moment. Nothing outside these walls was of any importance any more. The stresses and toils of daily living were high-class problems. It gives you a perspective.

It was like sitting on top of a mountain with no comprehension or care for what was going on down below. Your place in the world as you knew it simply did not exist then.

Danny had several visitors that Christmas day. Family and friends made an effort to put their normal Christmas day celebrations aside to spend time with us. Back then, I found it difficult to think outside the box. To see past my own pain, to notice how torn apart all our family and friends were. How much they loved Danny and their worries. My mind instantly told me that this situation was to be dealt with singularly by me and me alone. I can see now how this thought pattern emerged in me any time there was a crisis in our life to be dealt with. I turned into a lone wolf.

I did it without consciously being aware I was doing it, and the one person who was especially suffering from worry was my mother. My husbands' father had passed away five years ago and was still sadly missed. Ma had the worry for what her youngest daughter was going through as a mother. Also, the pity and concern for the suffering her youngest grandchild was enduring, and yet I refused to let my emotions reach out to how she was feeling. I was afraid to. Any image of my mother crying in my mind would put me over the edge for sure.

Thinking about it now, I realise that I knew her so well. She was my soul mate and for her to see us here huddled around our sick child in hospital on Christmas morning would surely break her heart, so intense was her love for us. With that in mind, I had told her earlier by phone that I would bring her up in the coming days. I always felt a strange sadness after a conversation with Ma, since all this had begun. This was a new emotion for me, which I didn't understand. On reflection, I have become aware that I was almost grieving for her.

My relationship with Mammy had changed of late. I had to stop needing her. Of course, I would always need my mother, but now only in a superficial sense. For the crisis I was in then I could not because I simply couldn't see her in pain too. Just as she could not bear to see me suffer, therefore, I could not turn to her in that time of need.

Ultimately, she suddenly stopped being the crutch I'd always leaned on my whole life. To my mind then, I had lost my comfort blanket. This knowledge was having a huge impact on me emotionally, although I didn't realise it then.

One memory that is most vivid in my mind from that Christmas morning was of my second-eldest brother Ciaran. As he was waving his goodbyes to Danny after visiting him, my poor child tried with all his might to raise his arm to return the gesture but could only make a feeble attempt. We had become accustomed to Danny's frailty, being with him daily, but my brother was clearly shocked. As I walked him out to the lift, he was silent.

'Are you okay?' I asked, concerned.

He sniffled in response.

I will never forget the look of despair on his face as he turned to me. Tears were welling up in his eyes, which he tried to hold back for my sake. He was heartbroken and speechless. This shocked me. I think because I had never seen tears in his eyes my whole life until now, we hugged our goodbyes. When the lift door closed, I stood in the hall and cried until my eyes dried up.

The snow fell heavily coming up to the close of this year 2009. Everybody who came into the ward made a comment about it. I did not witness much of it, nor did I care.

On New Year's Eve, around evening time, I had just arrived home when my friend Sarah phoned to invite the boys and me to her house for a while if we wanted to go. Her sons had received a pool table for Christmas, and she thought my boys would like to play a few games with them. I told her I would phone her back in a while. I couldn't form a rational decision. My mind was in a constant haze.

However, when I mentioned this to my sons, they were very keen to go, so we went.

My friend Sarah only lives at the top of our street, and I had decided that I would go only for an hour or so to please the boys. Unfortunately, that's not how it went. After getting settled with my boys and theirs all excited playing pool, my friends offered me a drink. Right then, my thinking turned. I suddenly announced to them, 'Please, don't ask me any questions or bring around a conversation about Danny now.'

They looked at me in silence.

'I just want to switch off now,' I ranted on. 'No positive clichés or encouraging words of hope for the future, please,' I urged them.

They had no reply. I think they were baffled by my outburst and simply nodded in agreement. At the time, I did not put much thought into my behaviour or try to reason as to why I was saying these things. I thought then that I simply needed to forget for a while. How insane that statement feels to me now as I write it.

However, knowing what I do now, the truth has unfolded for me. You see, I was in the company of alcohol. For me, alcohol and oblivion go hand in hand, and I wanted both right then. That being the case, the last thing I wanted to talk about was my very sick child simply because that would spark off a guilty conscience in my mind for being here drinking. Guilt and alcohol don't mix well.

I wanted to start as I meant to go on that night; get drunk, don't feel, selfish denial. I rang in the New Year in a haze of alcohol, consumed with destructive self-pity in its most soul-destroying form.

Mid-morning on New Year's Day, my husband arrived home. After greeting each other, he turned to me.

'Are the boys in their room, Mary?' he asked.

'Yes,' I said, 'Is something wrong?'

'Well,' he said. 'Sit down a minute.'

My body tensed immediately.

'Mary, Danny had another seizure last night. It was a very small one. It only lasted a few seconds, and he is fine now.'

My head went light, and that familiar ringing began in my ears. I put my hand to my mouth for fear I would scream. I looked at my husband, and he began to sob silently. I had no words of comfort for him. It tore at my heart to see his tortured face, and at that moment I hated myself beyond words for getting drunk last night without a thought for my sick child or his father on New Year's Eve.

I questioned myself, why did I do such a selfish thing? What have I turned into? Today I know.

The next day, as I sat at my son's bedside, the neurosurgeon came to us.

'Hello, Mrs McFadden,' she greeted me.

'Hello, Doctor,' I replied.

'I've come to tell you that we will be starting Danny on the treatment next week if he stays stable and does not contact any infections.'

I stared at her wide-eyed. 'That soon,' I said astonished.

'Well,' she replied. 'As you know, he had another small seizure last night. The sooner we try to shrink the tumour, the better for his comfort.'

'Try,' I repeated.

She stared at me nervously, I thought.

'There are never any guarantees, Mrs McFadden, but we will do everything in our power for Danny.'

Her voice sounded solemn to my ears. I put my head down.

'I know you will and thank you, Doctor,' I replied my voice solemn also.

'I just want to leave you this pamphlet before I go,' she continued. 'It gives some more information on the treatment Danny will be receiving.'

I took the pamphlet from her slowly, nearly recoiling from its contents. A terrible foreboding feeling came over me as I held it in my hand. As Danny slept, I opened the pamphlet and slowly began to read, with apprehension. I cannot recall every word, but I do remember vividly the shock that went through my body when I came to the page headed side effects. The words shook me to the core and sent shivers down my spine.

They read something like this:

Your child will experience nausea, sometimes severe, after treatments. He/she may have loss of appetite and hair loss. Your child may feel lethargic and lack energy. He/she must not be allowed to play any impact sport, i. e., football or soccer, and must keep exercise down to a minimum for the duration of his/her treatment.

Your child's abilities for school work will be affected, and he/she may need to be downgraded in school. Your child's growth may be stumped.

I had to stop reading. My heart was thumping in my chest. Never could I have possibly contemplated these horrendous side effects for my son, my beautiful, bright, energetic child. I had flashes of him coming through the door displaying the star on his school sweater for getting the highest result in an exam, the beaming proud smile on his face. I saw him playing soccer and rounders with his brothers and friends in the street. His friends cheering him on as he climbed nearly to the top of the street lamp delighted with himself because he was the only one who could make it that far up.

My head pounded as the despair rose inside. Tears blurred my vision as I tried hard not to scream. I shook like a leaf.

Suddenly, I was grasped by ferocious anger, of which I had never in my life experienced. For me, the shock of hearing my son had a tumour paled in comparison to the absolute heart twisting pain I was enduring with this news of the side effects of his treatment.

My anger rose repeatedly. I shouted in my mind, 'No, no, no!' as I shook my head from side to side. Not my child. Not this, please.

I began to tear at the pamphlet in anger and frustration. Ripping and ripping until it lay in shreds at my feet. As tears rolled down my cheeks, I put my head in my hands and in total desperation and anguish I began to pray.

'God, if you are there, please, please, don't put my son through this. Please, don't put him through this journey of agony ahead if it's to be in vain. I am begging you, God. If my son is to leave this world, please don't make him endure any more pain. Take him now. He has suffered enough.'

I slowly lifted my head, wiped my eyes, and taking my sleeping child's hand in mine, I kissed it as I sat silentlystaring out at nothingness. After arriving home from the hospital the next day, I felt deflated and exhausted. The adrenaline that seemed to be sustaining me through those dark days was evaporating, leaving me at the very least feeling melancholy.

I didn't tell my husband about the pamphlet simply because I did not see the sense in putting him through what I had experienced. I thanked my niece for taking care of the boys. I hugged her goodbye and went to spend time with my sons in their room.

We planned to take them up to see Danny the next day. We hadn't told them Danny had a tumour. We felt the word cancer would frighten them, so instead, we told them he had a brain disease that the doctors were going to treat the following week. There is no set rule for parents in these situations. In my opinion, it's an individual choice for each parent. For us, this was the best option to minimise our sons' worries for their brother's future.

I know as their mother, that if they knew then that Danny had cancer, they would surely fear that their brother would die. We wanted to protect them emotionally as much as we could at that time. Later that night, as I was tidying around, my phone rang. It was my husband's number. I froze.

'Hello, Dessie,' I said urgently. 'Is Danny okay?'

I heard him sigh. 'Mary, Danny is fine, but he has developed pneumonia. Now, don't panic. He is resting comfortably. He was coughing a lot, and they decided to X-ray his chest. They told me then that he has the infection.'

I was silent, numb, and deep in thought. My mind flashed back to the surgeon's words: 'If Danny does not catch any infection, we will start him on treatment.'

'Mary, are you there?'

I shook myself. 'Yes, I'm here.'

'They have put oxygen tubes in his nose and put an IV into his arm with antibiotics.'

'Is he awake now?'

'No, he is asleep, but he is okay, I promise. I'm here beside him. The thing is,' my husband continued. 'They can't start the treatment now, not when he has this infection.'

'I know,' I replied, almost whimpering.

'The doctors will chat with us tomorrow, they said.'

'Okay, Dessie,' I said. 'Are you sure he is not in pain?'

'I'm sure, Mary. I'll be beside him all night.'

'Give him a kiss from me,' I said through silent tears.

After I hung up, I fell into the chair and sobbed tears of guilt and despair as the reality of what I had prayed for was being answered. 'Don't make him suffer, God. Please, take him now.'

On the third day into the year 2010, my husband and I sat at the same table in the same room where we had been given Danny's diagnosis a few weeks previously. The same doctor sat across the table from us, hands clasped. Looking nervous, I thought. I knew this was not going to be good news for our child.

'Mr and Mrs McFadden, as you know, Danny has developed an infection in his lungs. For this reason, treatment is not an option for him. So far, there is no lifting of the congestion in his lungs with the antibiotic. Ultimately, if it worsens, he will not be able to fight this infection because of the limited brain function he has right now. As I had said to you,' she looked directly at me. 'Any infection would prevent treatment. Unfortunately, this has occurred now because his tumour has disseminated. It is slowing down Danny's organs from working effectively, which is why he can't fight the lung infection. Ultimately, his other organs will, I'm afraid, shut down rapidly also.'

'I'm so sorry to bring you this news. All we can do now for your son is to keep him comfortable and pain-free, which means a high dose of morphine. We will also put him into an induced coma to relieve him from the discomfort of enduring seizures. He will be moved to ICU today.'

She sat back in her chair, silent. The first thing I noticed was that my hands were numb from clenching the armrests. All I could feel or hear was the erratic thumping of my heart. I looked at my husband. He'd dropped his head in his hands and wailed as a nurse put her arms around him. I felt like I was observing all this rather than being part of it. It was as if it was all about someone else, not me or my son, although my body was shaking violently. I was suffering shock. I looked to my husband again in an attempt to do or say something, but no words came. I could not comfort him. I turned to the surgeon, and with a deep breath, I began to form a sentence.

'Doctor, please, exactly what does this news mean for my son?'

She leaned forward, hands clasped once more, and looked at me intensely, then sighed. 'I'm afraid Danny is now terminally ill,' she whispered solemnly. 'I'm so sorry.'

I sucked in the wail that tried to escape from my throat. 'How long does he have?' I managed to ask as calmly as possible.

'I can't answer that accurately for you.'

'Well,' I urged, surprised at my myself. 'Is it down to months, weeks, or days, Doctor?'

She sat back again and took a breath. 'I would be inclined to say days,' she whispered.

All I remember after that was the sound of ringing in my ears and my husband's cries. The next 24 to 48 hours in ICU were manic. Our son was now in an induced coma with one consolation that he did not have to endure any seizures. I cannot begin to describe what it feels like for a parent to watch your child suffer through that torture as you look on helplessly. It's a soul-destroying pain unique only to those who witness it.

Our son Danny was diagnosed on Christmas Eve. It was now 4 January 2010, and our baby boy was dying. Family and friends were constantly coming and going to the waiting room in ICU. Danny was on a ventilator, and our main concern right then was our boys at home. We needed to tell them their brother is dying, a member of staff trained in this area offered to do this for us. I instantly refused his help, thanking him.

'They need to hear this from us.'

I was willing to take her advice on how to word it to our boys. We were so nervous, so afraid of how our sons would be affected by the news. On reflection, the reality that my eight-year-old son was dying had not even impacted on me yet. I was in complete denial – aware of what was going on around me, but somehow feeling detached.

We were given a small room with comfortable sofas to talk to our boys. I don't feel I need to go into the details of the heart-wrenching news we had to deliver to them. Suffice it to say that their cries of despair and anguish tore into our souls bit by bit as we held them in our arms, telling them how sorry we were.

A short time later, the doctors and palliative care team held a meeting with us to give us the option of taking Danny home. This offer was a rainbow on the dark horizon for us. To get our child out of the hospital at last and home to everything he loved. His dog, his cat, his TV, his own bed, free from tubes and bleeping machines. Again, family rallied around for us preparing things at home.

I whispered to my child, 'Danny boy, you're coming home, son.

You're coming home!' Although he could not respond to me, I know in my heart, those words made him happy.

The snow was heavy on the ground as family and friends were all gathering around Danny in our sitting room. I took a quiet moment to stare out the window. I noticed then, Danny's friends and some of his cousins wandering about the garden very forlorn with their wee heads hung low. A tear fell from my eyes. I could almost feel their sadness. A thought came to my mind. I went to the front door and ushered them all to me.

'Do you all know what Danny would love you to do for him?'

They stared at me, shaking their heads in confusion.

I continued, 'He would love for you to build him the biggest snowman you can build right here.' I pointed to the middle of our front lawn. 'Do you think you could do that? It would make him very happy.'

Their eyes grew wide with delight.

'Yeah!' they screeched. 'We can. We will build the best snowman ever.'

Suddenly they were scurrying around, putting their gloves on, and within a minute they were all out on the green area in front of our home rolling snowballs. My two sons included. It gave them a sense of purpose, and they did indeed build the best snowman ever. I was overwhelmed with pity and pride for all of them.

It was bittersweet, to see the love with which they built that snowman for Danny boy, shining through.

The rest of that day and into the next brought a constant flow of family, friends and neighbours through our home. It was bedlam, and through it all I found myself on the outside looking in, detached. I spent most of my time consoling others rather than letting myself feel. I was on autopilot, in dangerous denial.

On the sixth of January 2010, as my husband, our sons and I were gathered around his bed, our youngest son Danny boy, took his last breath. His brief eight years on this earth ended. A light inside me went out, never to be rekindled.

Danny Boy was laid to rest on the ninth of January, which was the day of our middle son's eleventh birthday. The outpouring of love from Danny's school and football teams, from the whole community, was humbling.

Our son was loved and cherished by so many people, both young and old, still is today and forever will be.

Unfortunately, for me, the long torturous journey back to anything resembling quality of life had only just begun. Through the early weeks and months following Danny's death, I stayed in the state of denial that had functionally sustained me through his whole illness and death. I withdrew emotionally and began to block out reality. If I could pretend it did not happen, then it all might go away. I did not turn to the bed as I had been told some grievers do. Nor did I take care of myself, take things slow, eat healthily. I never returned to work.

What I did do was try to function as normal, doing all the daily chores, and cooking the meals for my family. I basically stayed detached from reality and emotionally numb. However, in order for me to sustain this free-from-pain state of mind, where I had subconsciously chosen to live, I needed a crutch, and that crutch was alcohol. Although, perhaps, as I reflect now and have an awareness of the disease, that sentence should be reversed. Rather, my alcoholism chose this traumatic time in my life, as justification to my consciousness, for me to lift a drink.

My common sense had told me that I was beginning to cross the line from being a controlled drinker to an alcoholic drinker. A short spell before Danny became ill, I was aware that since my teens, I had always used alcohol as a means of escape from a world that filled me with fear, and nothing ever feared in life could even come close to scratching the surface of the pain and despair hidden way at the back of my mind. Now, how would I ever be able to survive here on this earth, without my Danny boy? My beautiful baby son.

Chapter 5

Although family and friends kept in touch and visited regularly, our home felt empty, our hearts even more. Some days were simply an endurance for me. I was walking, talking, and breathing simply because I had to. There was no other reason. There was no substance to my life. I put the smile on, but underneath was a volcano of grief, distress, fear, hopelessness, heartbreak, loneliness, pain, and isolation. Also, add in a feeling of guilt around my excessive need for alcohol.

I struggled every day to try to keep this volcano from erupting. It left me emotionally bankrupt. We both did our bit for our sons to keep the bright side out. We went on two family holidays that year of 2010 — one to Lourdes in May and another to Tenerife with all our friends. The week break in Lourdes was compliments of the social club at my husband Dessie's company. I agreed to go only in respect for their generosity but with no enthusiasm. We did spend nice, needed quality time with our boys. I was grateful for that.

Danny's first Holy Communion day fell on the Saturday of the week we holidayed in Lourdes. That was a big relief for me, as I dreaded being at home on that weekend. The thought of spotting any of the children in our community or from Danny's class, dressed in their finery for their special day, tore at my heart because my child had been denied this big day. As it happened, Saturday came and went in Lourdes and thankfully, it didn't cross my mind.

In July of this same year 2010, we also went on a weeklong all-inclusive holiday to Tenerife, with our friends and their children. My husband and I had discussed it before booking and decided again to treat our two boys. All their friends were going, and they were very excited about going. By this time, it was beginning to be a real struggle to keep my constant craving for alcohol under control. I sustained my sobriety only when I needed to, but every night I drank and could just about curtail my intake to a bottle of wine.

The same applied for the full week in Tenerife. I was at the bar for a drink every chance I got. We did go on a few excursions, and our boys did enjoy the holiday, but I stayed emotionally detached most of the time. I put up a front when I felt I needed to for our boys but only really joined in the fun when we were all drinking.

My close friends Sarah and Katie and their husbands, Joe and Brian, noticed my excessive drinking, as too did my husband but everyone refrained from challenging me on it. Their solemn expressions when I arrived from the bar drunk, with yet another drink in hand, said it all. In hindsight, neither my husband nor I was in a fit emotional state to face a family holiday that first year after Danny's death in 2010. My husband Dessie showed integrity and selfless consideration for everybody else there, especially our sons, and hid his pain. I, on the other hand, held a what care I attitude, fortified by alcohol, drowning all my emotions in a bottle, with no thought of how it affected anybody, not even my sons.

My friends were very caring and regularly asked me if I was okay.

'Of course,' I always replied. 'Yes, I'm fine.' And I'd shrug off any opportunity for them to linger on, or open a debate on my excessive drinking. This they were aware of and backed off in respect for me. Sometimes, I tried to join in and feel part of the fun on the day trips, but it was futile. The cravings for my next drink clouded every day in every aspect. By the time we came home, my drinking had progressed rapidly. It was the only thing I looked forward to doing.

As my husband, sons, and all my family and friends pushed themselves forward to carry on, to face their daily responsibilities, I began to withdraw more and more. My drinking was ever progressing to a stage where I found it a struggle to get through a day without having a drink. I was jittery in the mornings and in a constant state of anxiety.

I tried my best to cover up my weakening mental and physical state when in the presence of my husband and sons, but inevitability the day came when I needed the morning after drink to calm my writhing nerves. Where I once used alcohol as the solution, I now drank not because I wanted to but rather because I needed to.

My body was in constant craving for the next drink. It became harder and harder to rise to my responsibilities as a mother and wife. Once my sons were secured in their rooms with their PlayStations after school, out came the bottle of wine, and I would sip away while preparing dinner. With every swallow, I began to relax more. Then I could take on any challenge. My drinking had progressed to an alarming level.

What I'm aware of now is the fact that Danny's death was merely timing rather than the cause. I had managed to keep this monster at bay during his illness and death, but only in so far as my cravings would allow. This day was always going to come for me, regardless of whether my son lived or died. I was always going to walk this path.

I know this because my pattern of thinking always led me to alcohol as my comforter. It was a means of escape from one fear or another. It was inevitable that the day would come when my crutch would become my crucifix.

In hindsight, I never had been a normal drinker. I just hadn't realised it. So, I continued to let my alcoholism fool me into thinking that it was fine for me to drink like that after all I'd been through. No thought came to mind for what my sons or husband were suffering. No, I'm an alcoholic. It's all about me.

My husband was worried and would question me, 'Are you drinking tonight again, Mary?' he would say in an exasperated voice.

'I'm only taking a few to help me sleep,' I would lie.

I could still somehow manage to conceal my alcohol intake during the day while he was at work. When he came home, I'd always make sure to be busying myself around the house, to avoid any closeness to him, in case he could smell my breath or notice my glassy, bloodshot eyes. Lying became part of my daily life. I became cunning and deceitful. All of these changes in me seemed automatic. I had lost my identity. I was a stranger to myself.

My friends started to notice. When I called to their homes for a social drink, I was already half drunk and never left without taking any remainder of my bottle home with me. I was thinking one step ahead constantly to ensure I had alcohol near to hand. In order for me to sleep at night, I had to make sure there was drink in the house for the next day.

I was slipping further and further into a dark hell in my mind, isolating myself more and more. This pattern of drinking continued into the weeks and months leading up to Christmas 2012. Although I was aware that my behaviour and manner had become warped, that I was drinking alcoholically, I could not find the courage to look at myself and face what I was becoming.

My mother and siblings would phone concerned about my isolation. I stopped visiting anybody and lied on the phone when they called saying I was tired or simply in a low mood — always using Danny's death as my crutch to continue drinking.

Nothing could be further from the truth, as I hadn't even begun to try to accept Danny boy's death. I was still in that absolute state of denial that my mind automatically tuned into since his diagnosis.

I was drinking because I was an alcoholic.

That's the truth, and that fact scared me to death. By then, I could just about hold it together to get my sons out to school and cook their meals. They distanced themselves from me and spent most of their time in their rooms, or at friends' houses. The same applied to my husband. We spent every evening separated. He would be in the sitting room and me in the kitchen, happy with my glass in hand.

For the last two years, I had built walls around me emotionally, brick by brick. I slowly began to hide inside these walls with all my fears and tears, but they were crumbling down at Christmas in 2012, revealing gaping cracks of grief, frustration, guilt, fear, worry and top of the list contempt for myself for what I had turned into, for what I was putting my sons and husband through every day.

All these emotions were being revealed to me in painful moments of clarity, which were too frightening to face. Therefore, I chose not to. I drank them away. I saw no way out, no way to repair the emotional damage I was causing.

After Christmas and into the new year of 2013, I became a morning-to-night drinker, totally isolated by my choosing. I could not let anybody see me. I ignored my phone calls, and except for staggering over to our local mini supermarket for my bottle, I never left the house. I rarely washed or brushed my teeth. Alcohol was ravaging my body, mind, and spirit, and still, I drank.

My sons had become used to coming home from school to see me drunk in the kitchen. I would greet them with big hellos and hugs while I staggered around them, slurring my words. They, in turn, would turn their back on me and go to their rooms and stay there until their dad came home. Most of the time, I would be in bed before my husband came home or be slouched on the chair in a drunken stupor.

He would confront me about my condition. I ignored him. My nervous shakes were that bad on awakening that I could not rise from my pillow without having several gulps from the bottle I had hidden under my pillow. The dry heaving was horrendous; even our family dog would run to safety when she heard me retching in the bathroom.

One particular Saturday morning, my husband was taking our middle son to a very important soccer final for his team, when they came through the kitchen, I tried to get up from the chair to give him my usual pep talk and a hug for luck. What happened then shook me from my drunken state momentarily. My child bent his head, stretched his arm out towards me with his palm up to my face in a 'stop' motion and walked past me out the door.

I stared at the closed door, floored by a flash of clarity. My thirteen-year-old son had shown me with that simple gesture, just how disgusted and disappointed he was in me as his mother. Although in that short space of time, I became riddled with shame, guilt and remorse for what I was putting my family through, I was too afraid to face up to it. I would not allow myself to feel the pain, to see the destruction I was causing them. When I looked in the mirror, I did not recognise the face that stared back. My appetite had disappeared. When I ate, I felt nauseous. I had gone down to seven stone in weight. I was in a savage state of mind, destitute physically and mentally.

Every penny went on booze. When I had no money, I would steal from my sons' small coin boxes. One particular morning of hell, I could not find any money anywhere. I was shaking so bad that I couldn't lift my cup of tea. I had to get a drink to calm my writhing nerves, to help me to breathe. I was sweating cold sweats.

Then, my eye caught the penny jar on the window sill.

Danny's penny jar!

Memories of my sweet child climbing up on the counter to take a few pennies for the shop for treats flooded my mind. The sound of his pockets jangling as he ran through the house. My throat became tight as I tried to swallow back the pain that was rising from my heart. To the normal-minded person, this moment would seem enough to wake you up to the reality of what you had become.

Not so to my mind, to the alcoholic mind. With tears rolling down my face, I took the lid from the jar and poured half the coins into a plastic bag. My hands shook so badly that I couldn't count out the amount I needed for my bottle. This was the power alcohol had over me. I had to relieve my rattling body. The only way was to get a drink. Nothing else mattered.

Staggering to the shop, I kept my head down as I entered. Darting straight to the wine section, I grabbed a bottle and went to the counter. By that time, the sweat was rolling down my cheeks, and my heart was racing uncontrollably. I mumbled my apologies to the young man behind the counter, and emptied the coins out in front of him, caring less about who witnessed me.

Lifting my head, I glanced to see his reaction, which could only be described as bewilderment. As he stared back at me aghast, I put my head down again to avoid his eyes.

'Do you expect me to count all this?' he retorted angrily.

I did not reply. I felt like I was on the verge of collapse. My legs went to jelly. I looked to the girl beside him at the counter with a pitying, silent plea.

'It's okay,' she whispered to her fellow worker. 'Give her the wine. I'll count the money.'

Mumbling a 'Thank you,' I grabbed my bottle and stumbled home as fast as I could, nearly collapsing onto the chair in my kitchen. I opened my bottle and drank until I felt my body relax, and my heart rate become normal.

That was my life then. I had lost my integrity, my morals, my respect for myself and everyone else – even those I loved dearly. A slave to alcohol, there I sat – dirty in the same sweater and pants weeks on end. Unwashed and empty inside. A shell of the person I once had been, yet I could see no way out. Being a wise, intelligent woman, I could not understand how I had succumbed to this – to allowing drink to take me to this hell I was living in. That's the only way I can describe my life then, a living hell, which my fears of reality kept me in.

I sometimes reflect upon myself then, my behaviour, my actions both verbally and physically towards the people I loved most in the world. My sons, who I would die for, who I had always tried to protect and shield from harm. My husband who then was also a shell of who he once had been, both in his grief for his son and then in his despair for what he had to face on a daily basis when he came through the door. For me back then, it was like an evil spirit had taken over my body and mind, and turned me into this monster I had become.

The things I did, the things I said, were the actions of something else, a demon. That demon came from a bottle.

Later that evening, I woke up from a drunken sleep shaking violently. Sweat oozed out of every pore. I curled myself up into a foetal position and began to whimper like a helpless puppy.

Something changed in my thinking as I lay there in despair. A flicker of light shone through the darkness in my mind and awakened my senses to the reality of what I was allowing alcohol to do to me. A sudden realisation that drink was going to kill me, hit me sharp between the eyes. This abrupt awareness filled me with immense fear.

Rocking myself as I held my arms across my nauseous stomach, I groaned, 'I can't go on! Please, God, if you're there, help me. I can't do this anymore, please, take over. I'm finished. I give up.'

I cried myself back to sleep.

'Mary, Mary.'

I opened my eyes to see my husband standing over me.

I noticed, for the first time since our child had died how drawn he looked. His eyes were bloodshot and sad. Emotions of pity and remorse rose in me. Before he could speak, I muttered in a daze.

'Dessie, I can't drink anymore, but I need help. I can't do it on my own.' Through my tears, I saw his face changing.

Suddenly his eyes brightened. He held me.

'Mary, we will get you all the help you need,' he sighed.

The next day I was driven by my husband to a treatment centre, fifteen miles from our home. My oldest friend, Ashling sat beside me.

Ashling and I had met and quickly became friends in the textile factory all those years ago. Our teenage years together involved having fun, partying and getting drunk. I was her bridesmaid. After I got married and had my children, we drifted. Ashling lived a few miles from my home.

She used to shop in the boutique I worked at in 2005, and we got back into each other's lives then. Ashling was also a sufferer of alcoholism and was in recovery when we met again. Thankfully she still is. She has been a tremendous support to me in my recovery, and we maintain a close friendship to this day.

My mind was in a haze, and I was extremely weak. My GP had given my husband medication for me, which was to be handed in when we arrived. I could not form a logical thought in my head, nor did I wish to. I had made a firm decision to keep my mouth shut, to let whatever may be just happen. Nothing that was ahead for me could ever be as bad as what I was leaving behind. With that knowledge, I was humble and willing enough to put my life into the hands of those who cared for me. I was at rock bottom. More than anything in the world, I wanted to stop drinking. I wanted a life back.

So, after a few weeks into the new year of 2012, I found myself lying in a strange bed in a strange place, away from my family, disorientated and completely lost. I was at the mercy of people I had never met.

The only thing that kept me going through the early days in the treatment centre was my visits from my loved ones at the weekend.

'Mary, is that your family in the corridor?'

I looked up from the table in the day room, where another patient and I were sitting playing Scrabble. Through the glass panel, I saw my mother and my sisters waving at me.

'Yes, it is!' I exclaimed with delight.

I jumped up and ran out to greet them. I was now midway through my twelve-week recovery programme in the treatment centre. Physically, I was strong now. There was also a tiny spark igniting inside my spirit, but I was still unsure about my mental state of mind. Most of my time there, I spent pining for my sons. I missed them so much, and as the alcohol fog lifted from my brain, the reality of what they'd had to endure from my behaviour constantly plagued me with guilt and remorse,

There was somewhat of a relief from this when I received their nightly calls. Nevertheless, I found myself needing to make it up to them somehow – to let them see that I could be once more the mother they deserved. These yearnings and negative thoughts held me back in my efforts to focus on the therapy I was receiving to help me to recover.

It was only later on in my programme, while listening to other patients' stories of their behaviour that I realised how lucky I was. I felt less burdened.

What most inspired me during my spell in treatment was the awareness that I was not alone in this hell of alcoholism, and nor was I a despicable human being,

For sure, I had behaved as such while drinking but through my counselling both group and one to one, I learned that alcohol had turned me into a savage – mentally, physically, and spiritually – and did not define me as a person. This gave me hope for a brighter future.

Some patients had lost everything and everyone through their drinking. They had their children removed, court appearances, homelessness, and even jail terms. Listening to their anguish filled me with a frightening awareness of what alcohol could do to you once you were drinking as an alcoholic. How it would strip you of everything until you were nothing. We all shared one common thread in this haven from alcohol; we had sunk to the point of no return. Even though we all came from different walks of life, hand in hand we were all trying desperately to claw our way back out of the alcoholic pit.

Some women were very well educated – teachers, journalists, nurses – some with master degrees, others had promising careers and financial stability, but ultimately all was lost in our drinking. This scary fact invoked a special camaraderie between us. Although strangers to each other, we shared a bond, an understanding of each other that was unique only to the sufferer of alcohol or drug abuse.

I met many beautiful, authentic ladies in this place and made several close friends who have excelled in their lives and careers in sobriety. We comforted each other in times of despair because we could all identify with the pain. Each one of us shared the same savage state of mind brought on by substance abuse.

There were two treatment centres adjacent to each other – one for the women and one for the men – and the only time we were mixed together was on Sunday when we were all required to attend church.

Visiting day was our highlight of the week, and it was held in the dining room.

'Mary, love, here's a wee parcel for you. It's only some underwear and a few pounds in case you need to buy anything.' My mother smiled at me as she handed me the beautifully wrapped parcel.

Thanking her, I hugged her tightly.

My heart was bursting with gratitude for the outpouring of love and support I received from family and friends but also a lot of guilt for my behaviour while drinking and for the upheaval it caused in their lives. It left me feeling inadequate and undeserving of the respect being shown to me. This guilt and remorse were at their peaks when my husband and sons would come to visit. They humbled me the most, for not only had they lost their brother, they'd also lost me as a mother. Their world had been turned upside down in the last couple of years of their young lives.

Yet the maturity they displayed, their compassion and selfless consideration for my dilemma, was truly something to be admired. Looking into their eyes, I was overwhelmed with love and pride for all three of them every time they came to see me,

These rainbow moments spent with my family gave me the resolve I needed to push forward in my recovery and persevere on in the treatment centre. I came to realise that my family were happier knowing that I was there getting well and that it would be futile for me to leave and return to them while still in the grasp of the alcoholic wiles and ways.

It would be best for them to have no mother than to be given back the excuse of a one who'd left our home a couple of months ago.

Lying in bed at night, I could see how alcohol had totally transformed me from a devoted wife and mother, a caring sibling, daughter, and friend into a self-obsessed, inconsiderate, hateful human being devoid of any emotion.

Where I once used alcohol to relieve me of insecurities, it now possessed me and stripped me from feeling any emotion whatsoever – such was its power over me. I was its prisoner, it my master.

In treatment, I was taught that not all is lost. That I could believe in myself again, and there were a lot of us out there, which helped me tremendously.

I would love to be able to write here that my life has been wonderful since my days in treatment. Unfortunately, that's not the case. I did experience a full year after leaving the treatment centre, which was alcohol-free. For various reasons, however, mainly consisting of procrastination regarding aftercare and AA meetings, at the age of 43, my fear of acceptance of my powerlessness over alcohol and other mental twists that I constantly suffered with, meant I was on a slippery slope in recovery.

There were a lot of demons I needed to face, which filled me with the worst of my stumbling blocks in life, which was fear. Nothing frightened me more back then than accepting that my son Danny had died.

I believe that from the moment my child had been diagnosed up until this time, I had buried all my crippling emotions deep into a crevice at the back of my mind. I simply refused to let myself feel the feelings. To the outside world, I was back flying fit again, ready to take on the world. In hindsight, I told myself that lie too. The more I convinced myself of this, the more my ego grew.

My enormous ego then told me that I could go this alone.

'Sure, I have mastered it. I am cured. I have conquered alcoholism.'

Subsequently, this pattern of thinking, along with my suppressed grief and fear of the unknown found me once again with glass in hand. Any fore boding thoughts of where I may end up if I drank, and what it would do to my family were pushed from my mind.

As my ego grew, those days of horrendous shakes and violent vomiting disappeared from my memory like mist in the sun.

That relapse lasted a couple of months and once again, I saw the pain in the faces of those I loved. Thankfully, I pulled myself up again from the brink. Perhaps, some of my teachings in treatment or my fleeting attendance to the fellowship of AA struck a chord somewhere in my conscience. In any case, I returned to my GP for help and went on a six-week detox programme with a local, addiction counselling service.

From there, I began the journey back to sober living once again.

When I reflect back on those fledgeling days early in my sobriety, I can see that my mind held a destructive set of thinking patterns that fear of change forced me to hold on to. Blocking out the fact that my son had died, I yearned for my old life back – getting drunk with my friends, calling my mother with a bottle of an evening for a catch-up – never once imagining that I could socialise like this without alcohol.

I also realise that within that first year of sobriety, I was living a lie. I was busying myself constantly so that I did not have to sit alone and think, going to our local pub with friends drinking non-alcohol beer, which I know now is a big red flag for me as an alcoholic. It tastes, smells, and looks like the real thing. It was simply a matter of time until it became the real thing.

I made another attempt at attending AA meetings, never allowing myself to feel part of the fellowship. Such was my denial.

This same year of 2014, at the age of forty-eight and two years after my spell in treatment, I got involved in charity work and once again busied myself daily. Still, at the back of my struggles lay denial – refusal to let my heart accept that my Danny boy had died. A refusal to let my mind accept I was an alcoholic. Moreover, I knew deep in my heart that with or without alcoholism as part of me now, my life had to change – my conception of what life should be like had to change.

Nothing could fulfil me now simply because my child would never be here on this earth again to share it with me, and nothing or nobody could ever take his place. Nothing frightened me more in my efforts at staying sober than facing this pain.

Ultimately, the ever-consuming fear that dominated most of my life was winning, but I trudged the road to recovery again by focusing on my sons and my husband. I was trying once again to make amends to them, and yearning to see their eyes shine once more.

Socialising without my crutch of alcohol was a huge struggle. For that reason, I needed to step back from spending weekends at my friends' homes. When drink was involved, I had been taught to prioritise my sobriety. This, I found hard. I'd feel left out and sorry for myself.

They would phone me regularly to ask if I would like to go out for a meal. They were trying to support me in my sobriety.

'Maybe next week,' was always my answer.

I chose to isolate myself. My thinking was obscured. I was holding on to a twisted sense of pride, embarrassed that I was now an alcoholic. 'They all pity me,' I would think. The truth is it was I who pitied myself, constantly nervous and edgy. My identity had been lost. I was filled with fear of the unknown.

Even when spending time with my mother, I felt awkward. So much had changed for the worst for all of us in the last few years. When in Mam's company, I felt like a disappointment.

In the early stages of my sobriety, I knew this was absurd thinking. My sweet mother was very proud of me and loved me no matter what, and I her, but that's where my mind was then. So, I put a barrier up. I pretended I was okay. That was a mistake.

My mother knew me better than anyone in the world. It would have been easier for both of us if I had been honest, broken down and cried, and reached for her comforting hug. I never did, and she never pressed me to.

I think fear held us both back. I was still very fragile emotionally but rather than reach out openly and express my feelings and fears for the future, I put up a front – a fake persona of strength and optimism – because although I knew my days were numbered if I continued drinking, I desperately clung on to the good old days in my mind. I wanted everyone to see me as I used to be.

I consistently tried to behave as the old Mary had. This was done out of fear of change. The new Mary, without her child, without her crutch of alcohol, frightened me so much. That denial was a safer bet for me back then.

The unchartered waters of grief and sobriety that lay ahead of me were simply too frightening for me to try to comprehend. I over thought everything, and when I wasn't doing that, I was overstretching myself physically, trying to please and make up for my wrongs, with my husband and my sons. I packed as much as I could in a day so as not to have to sit silently and think. I was pushing my reality to the back of my mind – engulfed in denial. That cloud of fear that had hung over me my whole life was raining down hard on my mind, blocking out any ray of hope that I could possibly face a new beginning of my life.

My mother was happy and relieved that I was sober, but I knew – without having to word her doubts to me – even she had her reservations about what my emotional state was. I could tell by her stare, and by her carefully chosen questions. She tiptoed around the word drinking.

While we were chatting over a cup of tea, she would inquire about my week and the boys, staying away from any topic around Danny or alcohol. The reason for this was she knew I had my guard up – my don't-talk-about-that attitude. I made sure I had plenty of small talk ready before I called at her house to keep her sidetracked from what was really going on for me. Like my friends on holiday, my mother sensed this. She knew I was avoiding the topics where her worries for me lay, but our eye contact spoke volumes to each other.

On St. Stephen's night of that year, 2014, after spending a lovely sober Christmas with my family, I was curled up watching a movie. My sons were at friends' houses, and my husband was at work. Out of nowhere, with no conscious memory of getting up from my chair, I found myself with glass in hand again.

When I reflect on this now, on how I was feeling, the only word I can think of is melancholy.

This time, for the time being, I could control my drinking. I became strategic, only drinking at night when I had the opportunity. How cunning alcoholism is. For I'd genuinely had no previous plan, or desire to take that first drink.

Fortunately for me, something was different this time. With every sip I took, there was fear. It just felt very wrong. Common sense was finally seeping in and making me aware that if I kept drinking, it would kill me and destroy my family for good. My thinking was changing this time around. It stayed very vivid for me. It switched from 'I want to be able to drink' to 'I cannot control my drinking. I want to stop.'

At that moment, on a nameless day in January 2014, the acceptance that alcohol controlled my life finally hit home. Alongside that thought came an instinctive drive to put the lid on it for good. Suddenly, I felt an inner strength and confidence erupting inside.

This time around, I found that instead of hating myself for failing again, I began to hate alcohol. I wanted more than anything to get it out of my life so that I might live again. This time I wanted my sobriety for me.

It was a strange mixed emotion, which is hard to explain in words, for I knew that by myself, I could not. But I also felt a sense of victory because by admitting and surrendering to my powerlessness, I had taken the first step to winning my life back. Humility came over me. It left me with a willingness and resolve to do whatever it took, with no reservations. That bittersweet rainbow moment was the beginning of my new life in sobriety.

To date, I haven't had another drink. As the saying goes, every journey in life starts with one small step. Moment by moment. One day at a time. I maintain my sobriety with the help of the fellowship of AA and by following a simple programme for daily living.

I have had many demons to face in my recovery. First and foremost, was the denial I held on to in respect to my son Danny's illness and death. Refusing to let myself feel this pain, it frightened me more than anything in the world, crippling me further and further into complete denial.

Now, in my recovery, I had been advised that the only way to move past pain is to feel it and let it go and that any emotion or negative thought that keeps me in a dark place in my mind can lead me back to the bottle. Having been given this information from wise, experienced sober alcoholics, I was only too willing to do whatever was suggested to maintain my sobriety. Never do I want to lift another drink.

An intention had to be made by me to begin my grieving.

This process required me to spend time alone. To allow the pain to come up, and to let myself feel it. I chose a weekend night when my husband was working, and my sons were out socialising.

That night as I lay in bed, I prayed to my child to protect me. Then I began to repeat to myself over and over, 'Danny boy is dead.'

Memories of my beautiful son flashed through my mind – his smile, his giggle, holding my hand, coming into the kitchen with a flower from the garden for me. There he was playing football on the street, with his brothers — climbing trees. The visions went on and on in my mind's eye. Then came the memories of him in the hospital bed, pale, thin, unable to speak. The seizures, the suffering he endured. Tears blinded my eyes. I did not cry but wailed in anguish. My throat became restricted. My chest tightened, and my breathing was erratic. All the symptoms I feared would befall me, did. I genuinely did not think I could survive this hopeless state of grief.

Realising then why I had hidden this horrendous pain for so long, my despair was such that I did not think I could survive without my Danny boy and yet what choice did I have? Eventually, I fell asleep on a very wet pillow. So began my journey of grief four years after my son's death.

The next morning, I awoke feeling drained and lethargic with a dull pain in my head.

The wonderful part was that I had no thought for a drink. This filled me with renewed hope, as I realised right then that, I was going to be okay.

I had faced the worst pain I would ever have to face in this lifetime, and I was okay. I smiled slightly as I got dressed at the gratitude and enlightenment that I became filled with because, instinctively, I knew that no matter what challenges life brought to my door, nothing could frighten me more than what I had endured that previous night. If I could stay sober through this, then what did I need alcohol for?

There are many days in my sobriety when the impact of my sweet child's death slams into my heart. I miss him so much. Sometimes it's like I'm in a twilight zone. That I'm here alive and breathing simply because I'm expected to be. I don't feel any purpose. In times like this, I sit in that pain. Let the tears of acceptance roll down my cheeks. This void in me where my child belongs is part of me, for the rest of my life.

I've learned to accept that also, this new me. I've had to. For too long, I tried to make life go away. When I couldn't, I drank the reality away.

I spent so many years of my precious life, pretending to be a certain person, to fit a set of criteria. It had been such a futile journey of frustration. I didn't need to do that anymore. I could put the cross down at last and embrace this new woman. That person that I used to be afraid to be.

Since I chose to live a sober life, one day at a time, I've had to make adjustments to my life. This involved not putting myself in a place or position where there would be any temptation to lift a drink.

One example of this was when my husband, the boys, and I were invited to our friend Sarah's barbeque. I was very aware that there would be a lot of drinking and it would be a long evening. This situation was going to be awkward for me in sobriety as I had experienced before.

While spending a long period of time in the company of alcohol with my friends, after a couple of hours in that environment, I could begin to get frustrated being the only sober attendant. This would leave me feeling sorry for myself, which in turn would make me feel resentful towards them for no reason other than the fact that they could drink and I could not.

These patterns of thinking are and were a huge red flag of danger for me in sobriety.

In the fellowship of Alcoholics Anonymous, I was shown how to live a content life by following a few daily principles to help me to change my thought patterns and behaviours. I needed to use these tools when up against anything that could frighten me into feelings of resentment, anger, frustration, self-pity, and many other fear-based ideas that came into my mind.

For that reason, I had talked with my friends and explained to them how important my sobriety was to me and how I needed to protect it at all costs. This meant not spending a dangerous amount of time in drinking circles, particularly in early sobriety.

Being the true caring friends they were, they understood, and although they did invite me to all their social occasions, they also respected me when I declined or stated that I would only attend for an hour or so, and wanted no requests to stay past my comfort time there.

This was how I maintained my contented sobriety. This too was a kind of grieving process, although in lesser terms, and it took a lot of work on my part to change how I perceived myself in this life.

Now, I must always try to think positively and never feed pity or resentment, and try to free my mind of those negative thoughts.

The biggest stumbling block for me was fear. These fears developed in me from the most trivial things, such as the simple act of asserting myself to my friends and family as with the social events, to the most frightening as in feeling accepting and releasing my pain in regards to grieving for my son Danny boy.

Fear has had an overpowering effect on me emotionally and mentally and had enslaved me all my life.

I had to – and did choose to – change totally if I was ever to feel any confidence at facing this life alcohol-free and be content. So, I have.

Letting go of old habits and thinking patterns was a must for me if I was ever going to be able to stay sober. I had to make a choice to steer clear of any event or situation that could send my thinking back to, 'Aw sure you can have one drink.'

If ever threatened by people, places or things, I had to remove myself from these situations, whether I liked it or not. I had to learn to accept this also. In turn, when I did the right thing, the right things happened to me.

Sometimes we don't get what we want in life, but I have learned that I get what I need when I'm willing to go the opposite way to where my old thoughts can take me.

For example, I used to think that a party wouldn't be a party without me in the mix, or I would feel that I had to be where my friends or family were in a social setting because I didn't want them to be enjoying themselves without me being part of it all.

All these mental twists I had, needed to be banished from my thoughts. It was very hard to let them go, but I knew this was the only way to protect my sobriety, and for me to drink is to die.

I have surmounted so many challenges in sobriety, both personally and socially; things that I never dreamed were possible for such an insecure, frightened girl like me. Some of these milestones may not be so daunting for the average person. For me, though, they were mountains to climb, without my crutch.

Simple things like holding a conversation, dancing at social events sober, sitting at a table talking about myself in front of a room full of people, speaking my mind assertively, singing in a choir in front of an audience, enjoying weddings, Christmas parties, sober, jumping out of a plane, and, of course, writing this memoir.

With every hurdle I jumped in sobriety, I gained more confidence, more humility, and more gratitude.

The best gift I have been given in sobriety, however, is the release from my crippling fears; those fears that dominated and held me in their grips for most of my life.

How did I achieve that? Well, the answer is simple: I faced them.

Although it sounds obvious to the normal-thinking person, for me anything that required me to be assertive, brave, or in the limelight in any situation terrified me. It filled me with panic, and, therefore, I learned from a young age to avoid at all costs where ever possible any situation or person who brought that confidence-shattering fear to the fore. Being a recovering alcoholic has meant that I needed to face this major handicap I suffered with.

To address my fears, I firstly had to admit them to myself and to another person, which I did in counselling sessions while in treatment.

As I have expressed, my social skills were non-existent. Weddings, funerals, social get-togethers including a simple coffee morning sent a shiver of tension down my spine because my self-esteem was so low. I simply did not feel connected. I had a sense of being set apart from society and was constantly on edge.

I can only explain it as something similar to watching a horror movie, where you know that any minute something is going to happen and frighten the life out of you. That feeling was as close as I can get to describing how I felt when in a group of people or in a situation where the spotlight would be on me in any way, shape or form. Even simple conversations where I may be asked for an opinion filled me with dread.

There was no doubt that the embarrassing blushes I suffered with are a major factor in my personality flaws and contributed hugely in my avoidance of being in the spotlight.

I would analyse any upcoming event or social gathering with a negative mindset. I would be saying to myself, 'What if I blush? Then everyone will notice. I'll feel like a fool, and then, and then, and then, ad infinitum.'

The thing was, I never once said out loud or to myself, 'I'm afraid', and that's because I was afraid to say I was afraid.

In the past, I could mask fear with alcohol. Now, I don't have alcohol, but I still have fear. As advised by councillors and my fellow sufferers in the fellowship, I was now aware that I had to face these fears head-on. Although I was frightened, I knew if I kept avoiding everyone and everything that put fear in me, I could never stay sober. Or perhaps I might stay sober, but I would have no quality of life.

Ridding myself of it was a huge challenge for me. Anything that took me away from the security of my family home and close friends, both in childhood and adulthood, set off alarm bells in my head and my deep-rooted fear came to the fore, crippling me with anxiety,

As the years passed, this fear manifested itself in several ways through my personality. What helped me to change most was the significant positive mantras I heard in the fellowship of AA. For me personally, by working on suggestions given to me, I slowly and sometimes with self-pity and frustration, began to face fear on a daily basis.

The way I did it was by talking to my self before whatever may have been coming up that I felt anxious about, or a responsibility I felt I needed to rise to.

I would say, 'Now, Mary, you're afraid of this, and that's okay, but it's not okay to hide in your fear. It's not okay to let fear have power over you anymore. It's time to face it head-on and hope for the best. Sure, what's the worst that can happen?'

This was my mantra now, and to my delight, it worked. My fear diminishes a little more every time I don't allow it to stop me from joining in with the human race without the crutch of alcohol to hide behind. The most amazing part is that the more I face anything that challenges my confidence, the more confident I feel for achieving it. It, therefore, keeps me further away from any notion of lifting a drink.

Since I am coming to realise that I can live a fulfilling life without the aid of alcohol, well then why would I need a drink?

Gaining acceptance of the fact that my youngest son Danny had died was and still is the hardest challenge for me and the most painful. It is the knowledge that I have to face life here on earth without ever getting to see my beautiful child again.

The only fear I hold with regard to this is that I would try to alleviate the anguish by drinking because let's face it, I have hidden in a bottle over many less trivial challenges.

One of those challenges was the fear of taking our family dog for a walk alone, which I had never done, nor was required to as my husband and sometimes our sons held that responsibility.

Our dog is a wee collie named Clyde. We took her home twelve years ago after a family visit to our local dog pound. She was only four months old and part collie and spaniel. She has more collie traits, though, with a long-haired black and white coat and a very loving personality. She was wise and totally devoted to us as her family. We love her dearly.

She always loved spending quality time with our boys and had a particularly special bond with our son Danny.

Since his death, we as his family have often talked about how protective our wee dog was over Danny. She would jump all over him in excitement and joy when Danny came through the door from school. Danny used to giggle at that. Our collie would almost knock him over in an attempt to get into his arms.

But her protectiveness over our child was unique. She would throw herself across Danny on the sofa if ever any of us went to approach him. Our older sons used to find this very amusing and would often reach for Danny on the sofa when Clyde, our collie was sitting beside him, just to see the reaction of the dog.

The minute my older boys went to grab at Danny, Clyde was across the sofa and planted herself on top of Danny, smothering him under her hairy coat.

She would look at the boys with a stern eye. It was her way of saying, leave Danny alone. I have often shed a tear, remembering those times when sitting alone on the sofa with our wee dog. I have wondered if she was missing Danny boy. She clearly loved him dearly.

The strange thing was that I had never developed any fear of being around dogs since the attack I suffered when I was a young child. Perhaps this was because we, as a family, in our childhood, always had a family dog as a pet. We had a collie ourselves when I was a child, and we loved him. He was already a big part of my life at home before the dog attack, and I was still fine around him and other friends' dogs after the attack.

The only time I was cautious was when I was introduced to a strange dog. I would tense up but only momentarily. Once I realised the dog was friendly, I was fine.

Certainly, there were occasions where my friends and I would be calling for another friend, and I would hear their dog barking at us from the back garden. The sound of the dog's barking and aggressive voice would freeze me with fear, but I knew I was safe, so the fear subsided quickly.

I was and still am very cautious and nervous around Alsatians. I don't see them very often, but when I do, I tense up. They are beautiful animals, but all I can focus on when I see one is their sharp teeth and large mouths. I have no trust around them.

The only bone shattering fear I still had as regards to dogs, and still do, is when I hear or witness them fighting. That snarling, angry, aggressive sound they make just frightens the life out of me

Any time I've had to witness any dog fighting since my attack, I've had to run for my life with my hands over my ears. I simply can't bear it. My heart races and I shake from head to toe. How this happened to be, I don't know, but that is the only scenario where dogs are concerned where I felt traumatised from that day forty-four years ago.

My husband was very aware of my fear around going out alone with our dog. When I mentioned to him that I wanted to start facing this fear, he was wary for me, for how it would affect me. He told me I didn't need to do it. He could take care of the dog-walking duties.

Once I explained why I needed to face this fear, he was supportive.

Now, I need to say here that the very thought of doing this seemingly menial task, scared me senseless. It was the thought of meeting another dog in the street that scared me. What if I met an Alsatian on our walk? Maybe another dog not on a leash, and that dog might attack my dog.

That was where my crippling fears lay. I spoke to myself, saying my mantra. 'Mary, it's okay to be afraid, but you need to do this. It's time to face this fear.'

With my iPod on and my earphones in, I left our home one day after taking countless deep breaths. This was about three years ago on an October morning. There was a sharp wind. I put on my gloves and took hold of my collie's lead. With trepidation and worry, I opened our front gate. I was so afraid. I looked up and down the street several times in case there were any dogs roaming freely around. I looked down at my dog's face. At the same time, she looked right back up at me. We stared into each other's eyes for a moment.

Suddenly, I felt this strange sensation of serenity. As I gazed into my wee dog's bright brown eyes, her stare calmed me somewhat as I realised how much this short walk meant to her. She expected so little from me and in contrast, she had given so much through her loving companionship and devotion to me. Bending down to rub her head, I whispered, 'Okay, Clyde. It's you and me against the world now. Let's do this'.

I'm afraid I would be telling a lie if I were to say that I enjoyed walking my dog that first day. On the contrary, I was frozen in fear, but I trudged on.

We came across several dogs on leashes with their owners, and I held my breath, giving them a wide berth as they passed us. I would take my dog out on to the road so as not to have to pass them in close proximity.

My poor dog was very confused by these manoeuvres as were the other dog owners. A couple of them when realising what I was doing, quietly said in passing, 'There's no need to be afraid. My dog is very friendly'.

I nodded my response with my head down, embarrassed by my behaviour.

Thankfully our wee dog Clyde was very easy going and did not feel threatened by other dogs, so there were no scuffles. That was a major relief for me.

I practically ran the stretch from the top of my street to my front gate with Clyde trotting along beside me. Afterwards, I sat in my kitchen breathless and shaking but with a huge smile on my face. The confidence boost I had gained from achieving that task – facing that lifelong fear – was euphoric.

As my collie Clyde curled upon the sofa in our kitchen, I went to her. Rubbing her ears, I said, 'Thanks, Clyde, for encouraging and protecting me today.'

She lifted her head slowly and gazed at me.

I was tearful with fulfilment.

I have taken Clyde for several walks since that day, and although I still feel somewhat like a frightened child during the process, it does not matter. What does matter is that I am determined to diminish and hopefully, eventually, banish all my negative soul-crushing fears from my life, for once and for all. I will do this with a strengthened, confident resolve to take my power back so that I can concentrate on staying recovered from the one thing that I will never have power over, that's alcohol.

Each time I faced one fear, I gained more confidence. I would sit silently afterwards and smile feeling fulfilled.

The social side of life in sobriety was and still can be a huge obstacle for me without my crutch alcohol. This was simply because of my absolute lack of confidence but I had to overcome fear, and I was determined

My first challenge in this area came in the early days of my present journey in recovery. I was asked to chair at a meeting in the fellowship of our local AA on a midweek night. I felt my heart skip a beat the minute after the request. My initial thought was 'Say no,' but I remembered the advice given to me, 'Go against yourself.'

I said yes, giving no thought to what effect this challenge would have on me. I busied myself for the whole day and refused to let fear take hold although I was extremely nervous.

I sat in the chair that night and shared my experience to a room full of silent onlookers. I forced myself not to over think what was going on.

To my astonishment, the words flowed from my lips with very little effort on my part. I almost felt alienated from myself as I sat there talking. I do not recall the words I spoke, but what I do remember was the feeling of euphoria afterwards. In my wildest dreams, I could never have envisioned myself doing anything remotely as nerve-wracking as that even with alcohol in me, let alone sober.

This woman who had lived in the shadow of fear all her life – who had hidden from society until she was drunk enough to pretend – seemed to have been lifted out of the chair that night and a total stranger put in her body. I remember going to bed on that wonderful night feeling so grateful, so content, and confident. I never imagined sobriety could give me this peace of mind and body.

I decided there and then that I would continue to fight my fears with all my might; that I would push myself beyond any boundary so as to hold on to that feeling. I made a resolution never to let fear stop me again, unless, of course, there was danger involved. As crazy as this may sound to some, I realise now that if I was not an alcoholic, had never walked through the doors of AA for help to recover, I doubt very much that I would have searched for a solution to my underlying fears, nor would I have addressed them.

I had gone through my whole life, adjusting my emotions to suit the outside world's expectations of me, never being able to discover my potential because I was afraid. My sensitivity and lack of confidence were all based on fear.

There was the fear of ridicule or condemnation. Criticism or humiliation stopped me in my tracks, denied me happiness, joy, peace, or contentment in life. It left me frustrated, lonely and consumed in self-pity. Although I masked my emotions for the benefit of others, when alone with silence all around me, I felt an emptiness inside, there was a void in my soul. There was a part of me who was fearless, creative, wise and intelligent, but those fine qualities were hidden, forbidden from being shown to the world because fear had power over them.

In sobriety, I have had the opportunity to analyse myself as a person – my pitfalls and character defects – with a lot of help from the fellowship of AA and a supportive family, a few friends and much hard work mentally. I now look at my actions on a daily basis; with humility and being honest with myself, I try to correct any areas where I'm selfish or self-centred. In turn, I can change these flaws by being helpful and selfless and so transform my life positively.

I could never show enough gratitude to my loved ones, and especially my husband and sons, for standing by me through the hell I put them through on a daily basis with my drinking. I strive now every day to try to do my best to help them and others, to put other people's needs before my own – except when guarding my sobriety, this must always come first, for me and for the sake of my loved ones. The astounding fact is that being an alcoholic and reaching out for help to recover has given me a life beyond my wildest dreams, not in the material superficial sense. Better than that, it has shown me how to be me.

It is slowly banishing fear from my life one day at a time. I truly believe that I have been given two lives in one lifetime. For this gift, I'm eternally grateful. I grasp this chance to live again with hands on heart. The hard work was worth it all. Simply put, it's FREEDOM.

***

Being sober does not protect you from the hardships and traumas in life. My mother was diagnosed with chronic, obstructive, pulmonary disease (COPD) in 2014, and as it gradually progressed, it left her short of breath. She also began to suffer dizzy spells, which left her afraid to leave the house as time went on, in case she fell, which she had done on several occasions.

All that aside, she was bright and had all her faculties. She loved our visits to her home. She was always curious about how our week had been and loved a good old chat. Mam never complained or moaned about her declining health. She was always the optimist. Within the last twelve months of her life in 2016, however, her health declined rapidly. Her appetite ebbed drastically also, and she became very frail and thin. During these months, I found it very difficult to watch her decline. As the year went on, she began to suffer memory loss too. My siblings and I were worried.

My mother was obstinate and strong-willed and getting her to go to her GP was an all-out battle of wills between us. This was particularly with my eldest sister Lizzy, who looked after Mam most of the time. Through all her discomforts, though, she held on to her sharp wit and humour.

On one occasion over this year, after a visit to the GP, which she very reluctantly agreed to, he advised her to eat fruit, particularly oranges. Naturally, we all brought her oranges when we visited her.

This was fine for about a week or so, then one Saturday, I arrived at her home, and after we greeted each other, I handed her a punnet of small oranges. I could tell immediately by her expression that something was wrong. She forced a smile as she thanked me in her usual manner. As I sat beside her on the sofa, she turned to me.

'Mary, love,' she said, almost whispering in case anyone could hear her. 'I don't want to sound ungrateful or anything, and thanks, love, for the oranges but something is wrong with everyone.'

I looked at her puzzled. 'What do you mean, Ma?' I said.

'Mags, everyone is giving me oranges,' she exclaimed dumb founded. 'Lizzy, Erin, Joseph, Ciaran, all of them. They're all handing oranges to me. I know they mean well and I appreciate them all being kind to me,' she continued. 'But, sure, there's only so many oranges a woman of my age can eat,' she said baffled. 'Now, don't tell the rest of them I said that, Mags.' My mother looked at me with her stern-eyed expression. 'I don't want them thinking I'm ungrateful.'

I looked into her beautiful blue eyes, now glassy and tired-looking, and I smiled at her.

'I won't tell them, Ma, and only eat as many as you can. You don't have to eat them all.'

'I'm not,' she replied. 'I'm giving most of them to Benji when nobody is looking,' she replied slyly.

Benji was my mother's wee terrier dog. She loved him dearly. This was just one example of the kind of person my mother was; humility and gratitude were just some of her many qualities. She would accept and endure anything rather than hurt anybody's feelings, even over an orange.

Within the last six months of 2016 and into the first half of 2017, my mother's health really took a downward spiral. We were worried because she had practically taken to her bed now. She was extremely weak but still her usual bubbly self when I visited. Sometimes, I would look at her in a silent moment between us as I sat at her bedside. She would stare out her bedroom window, and I could see sadness and even fear in her eyes. Then, as quick as lightning, she'd bounce back again.

I would sigh when I witnessed this. I knew deep down that my mother's time would soon be up on this earth and in those moments, as she stared out her window silent and melancholy, I knew she did too.

On some of my visits, I would take down my Scrabble game to her. My mother was a whizz at crosswords, but of late she could not concentrate enough on them. I decided to try playing Scrabble with her. On the first visit with my game, we got started. To my total surprise, she had a six-letter word on the board in less than a minute.

I looked up at her bewildered. 'Ma,' I said. 'Well done. That was quick.'

She returned my stare looking confused. 'What do you mean, Mary? Sure that's only a wee word. A child could get that one.'

I nodded at her and smiled.

I was speechless and very impressed. My mother always impressed me.

During the latter part of her life, I found it hard to leave her after a visit. It was frustrating and heartbreaking to see her a shell of the amazing, bright, charismatic lady I was proud to call my mother. It hurt to see her in her fragility. Mostly, I was sad for her. Her quality of life by then was non-existent, and I hated to picture her lying in that bed, day in day out. I would come home in a very low mood. It was just another example in my life of a situation I had no control over, and it brought back memories of my son Danny in his last days in the hospital.

On 24 July 2017, my mother was admitted to hospital. My siblings and I became very worried about her as she could not stand unaided by this time. I went with her in the ambulance. She was chatty and bubbly all the time, but her words were slurred,and she was extremely disorientated. She also seemed to slouch to one side a lot.

I mentioned this to the nurse once Mam was settled into a bed in hospital. She said that the doctors would check her out and likely do X-rays on her lungs and chest, and some blood tests. The next evening on 25 July, my husband Dessie and I went up to visit Mam. On our arrival, we were taken aside by a doctor before we got to my mother's ward. After introducing himself, he asked if we were family.

'I'm her daughter,' I said warily, and this is my husband.

'That's fine,' he said. 'I need to talk to you then about your mother's situation.'

We were silent in response.

'We have done X-rays on your mother's chest and, by my request, we have also done a scan on her liver,' he said in a quiet, calm voice. 'I'm afraid the results are not good.' He paused before continuing. 'Your mother has several tumours in her lungs, and her right lung has collapsed, which is the reason for her leaning onto her right side.' He said solemnly, 'She also has tumours on her liver.' The doctor paused then to let us absorb the news.

I looked at my husband. He returned my stare as he put his arm around me. I had no words. I simply wanted the doctor to continue telling me what I deep down already knew.

'So, Doctor, what is her prognosis?' I asked, almost impatiently. I felt like I was almost transported back in time to Christmas 2009 when we were being told of our son Danny's fate. When I looked at my husband, I saw in his eyes the same emotion. It left me fearful of how I could contain myself. I almost wanted to run away.

The doctor put his arm on mine. I tensed immediately.

'I'm afraid,' he began in that familiar solemn tone that seems natural to their vocation. 'We cannot treat your mother, and operating is of no use either in her case. She is too weak and frail for either.'

It was almost surreal for my husband and me, hearing these words, and I found myself repeating my son Danny's name in my mind.

The doctor continued as we stood speechless staring at him. 'We could do a biopsy on your mother tomorrow,' he said. 'But I really don't see the point in putting her through the discomfort of this. I know what I see, and I'm afraid the best we can do now is to keep her comfortable and out of pain.'

I took in a deep breath and calmly said, 'How long does she have left, Doctor?'

He paused for a moment and then replied almost in a whisper, 'I would say no more than a few days. The cancer is very aggressive.'

I felt my husband's arm tighten around my shoulders, but the strange thing was, I was calm. It surprised me how grounded I felt. The fear I had felt coming over me minutes earlier diffused in me. It was like I had already known I was going to hear this news; as if I had been prepped for it almost, which I suppose I was. My husband also. We had walked this tight rope already.

'Doctor,' I said presently as he waited patiently for our response. 'Is my mother in any pain?'

'That's the strange thing,' he replied. 'She only asked for a Panadol for a rash she has on her backside.'

I actually smiled at this statement as the doctor looked at me almost bewildered.

'That's my mother,' I said with a tear in my eye.

'She is a strong woman,' the doctor said. 'I don't advise that you tell your mother about her diagnosis,' he said. 'I see no point in worrying her at this stage. We have told her she has a chest infection which we will treat. We will put her on morphine, which will relieve her from pain and also keep her in a sleep state.'

The doctor then bent forward close to my face and said in a whisper, 'Go in there and make your mother smile.'

We did just that.

My husband and I gathered all my siblings together at my sister Lizzy's house that night and told them the news. Silence was all around as they each tried to absorb it in their own way. Some cried. I cried.

Some kept their composures and bottled emotions for another time but ultimately for all of us, thoughts of losing our mother were heartbreaking. We all treasured her dearly for our own personal reasons. As our mother, she had a special role for us individually.

The next couple of days at the hospital, we all rotated as a family to have someone with my mother at all times. She was admitted to hospital on 24 July, and two days later on the 26th, she was unconscious and on a very high dosage of morphine. On the night of the 26th, my siblings and I were discussing who would stay that night with her. My husband and I said we would stay. My husband worked a shift rotation and was off work the next day, so it was convenient for him to stay with me.

We sat with her in turns, and when it got late into the night, we lay across the chairs provided in the hallway outside the small room she was sharing with another patient. At 3.30 am, I woke up after having a vivid dream. My mother had been speaking to me. I went into her room and sat beside her. I didn't bother my husband, who was still sleeping in the hallway. As I sat there at her bedside, I rubbed her thin forehead and assured her I was with her, whispering into her ear.

Suddenly, a huge sadness rose in me and with it frustration and slight anger at the injustice to my mother, that she was enduring this prolonged suffering. I looked at her thin face, her snow-white hair, and then I saw how laboured her breathing was. I sighed with sadness and pity for my beautiful mother.

A sudden thought then came to me. I looked at my watch. It was 3.45 am. Suddenly, I found myself praying in a very similar fashion to the way I had when I'd known what lay ahead for my son Danny.

I said, 'God, it's now 3.45, and my mother has been suffering for three days now. Please, stop this. Please, don't make her endure any more. She has risen to all her responsibilities in life. She has done what you needed her to do. If you're there, please, end her suffering. That's enough, God. That's enough. Let this stop by 4 am, please.'

This mantra just fell from my lips, such was my anguish, knowing how much my sweet mother was enduring lying there. I bent in close to my mother's ear. I said to her, 'Mam, it's okay to stop fighting now. Let go, Mam. We are all okay here, and we will be fine, Mam. We will help each other. You don't need to worry about us, I promise. You have been through enough. Stop fighting now. Let go, Mam.'

These words and prayers I said then were in desperation and just seemed to come to me for that reason. When I sat back, I noticed my mother's breaths coming quicker. Her jaws being sucked in with each laboured breath. Within a minute, she stopped. It was over.

I sucked in a breath myself. Tears welled in my eyes. I bent forward and kissed her on her forehead. 'Tell Danny boy we love him, Mam. Give him a hug and a kiss,' I whispered through my tears. 'Goodbye, Mam. I love you.'

My mother died on 27th July 2017 at 4am, aged 79.

I'm still unsure of where I am regarding my grief for her. For me, personally, it was more painful to watch her failing than it was to see her lifeless.

This authentic, beautiful lady had always been, and always will be my strength and inspiration. Sometimes, I feel like she is living inside me, spurring me on. It was with my mother in mind that I opened my notepad and began to write this book.

My soul mate in life, she possessed unique wisdom. This was her overall special quality. Sometimes when she looked at me with her striking blue eyes, I felt like she could see right into my soul.

She kept her spark alive – her witty personality – almost up until her death. Her motto through the hardships she endured in life was always, 'Sure, it could be worse.'

Sometimes at night, I would have memories of her standing at the sink in our wee kitchen, peeling potatoes, or leaning over the old washing machine, surrounded by a mountain of dirty laundry. She would have a faraway melancholy look on her face.

Remembering these times makes me sad. I have so much pity for her, for the cross she had to bear, but I truly do believe she is at peace now, and that her light shines now in me. That everything she would have liked to achieve in life, she now urges me to achieve, both the simple and the challenging. I can never praise my sweet mother enough. Yet she was humble and grateful and devoted to her seven children. The strongest woman I knew and, my closest friend.

My family have reaped the rewards of my sobriety also. Although in the early stages, there was tension in our home, the trust had gone and took time to rebuild. I had let them down so many times; myself also.

Now, in my recovery, I needed to take responsibility for my wrong doings, to own my mistakes, and apologise for them. Only then could I expect them to believe that I had changed and was truly sorry for everything I had put them through and thus empty myself of the guilt and remorse that if held would likely lead me back to lifting another drink.

Sitting with them one by one, I made my amends. As ever being the beautiful human beings, they were, inside and out, they accepted my apologies with gratitude that I had my life back together again. My eldest son Ryan's reaction, in particular, blew me away.

After apologising to him, his reply was, 'Okay, Mam. Now, will you do me a favour?'

Silenced, I replied, 'Yes, Son, of course. What is it?'

'Please, don't feel guilty about any of it, Mam. We are fine now, and everyone makes mistakes.'

I choked back tears when he said these words. My love, pride, and admiration for this precious young man were beyond words. This was yet another rainbow moment given to me, ever strengthening my resolve to stay sober.

I've had many amends to make in my journey of recovery from alcoholism, not least to the poor young man who served in our local shop, the one whom I'd left standing aghast when I threw the bag of pennies on his counter for my bottle of wine.

He too, like everyone else accepted my apology with a smile saying, 'Don't worry about it.'

I was blessed with the reactions I received and very humbled.

The things I did and said and the things that I refused to do while drinking, were completely alien to the standards I had set for myself to uphold everyday previous to this. Alcohol had taken over my body, mind, and soul. Nothing had mattered to me. It was like having a death wish. I simply became evil to the core. My mind became diseased and twisted. I obviously don't know what hell is like, but if it centres in the mind, alcoholism is as close as it gets to being there.

Once I'd crossed the line from controlled drinking to full-blown alcoholism, I not only lost the power of choice, I'd lost my sanity as well. I had absolutely no shred of common decency left in me, and because I had gone temporarily insane, I had no comprehension of that fact. This meant that the wife and mother whom my husband and children knew and cherished, had been taken out of their lives and in her place, there sat a sadistic, selfish, inconsiderate, cold, and heartless monster.

While I was in that savage state of mind in my alcoholism, reality did not exist for me. I had no concept of days nights or weeks. I simply drank and slept towards the latter end. However, my husband was very aware of what was happening to me and the effects it was having on him and our boys at home. We have talked about this since my recovery. I needed to hear what daily life was like for him back in those years of 2011 to 2014, in particular, and he needed to vent it. This was the only way to put it behind us and strive to have a healthy relationship in the future.

It has been four years – as I write here in 2019 – since my last drink, and only now are we both comfortable and trusting enough to talk openly about it.

When I gave my apologies to my sons for what I had put them through, they were amazing in their response, telling me that they were just glad that I was sober now. For my husband and I, however, we felt that for us to start afresh, he needed to express how my behaviour had been pushing him over the edge as regards his respect and love for me. As we sat alone over coffee on a quiet weekend night in our home, our boys were out socialising, my husband began to tell me his story.

'Living with you then, Mary, was like living in a daily nightmare. I never knew what I was going to greet when I came through the door. I was constantly on edge. It was like living in a fire station waiting nervously for the fire alarm to ring.

When I was at work, I worried about what state you were in at home and what the boys would see when they came home from school. I couldn't get through to you. You just ignored everything I said. It was like talking to a zombie.

The only time I could relax was when I was asleep, but the minute I opened my eyes, the nightmare started again. I saw the wife I knew disappearing before my eyes more and more every day. You were fading away with drink, and I could not do one thing to stop you.

I reached out to your family, and some of them felt that the best thing for the boys and me was to put you out of the house. I couldn't do that. They really didn't understand your disease, and neither did I.

I was worried more when I woke up, and you were not there, and you had the car. I'd be frantic in case you crashed and killed yourself or some innocent person drinking and driving. That's when I started to hide the car keys. All I felt I could do then was try my best to be there for the boys and just let you be to find your own way.

It broke my heart looking at you destroying yourself, but I had to accept that I could do nothing about it. So I talked to the boys explaining to them that you were sick, that you did not mean to hurt them, but you were an alcoholic and were not thinking straight. They accepted that, but I told them to stay away from you as much as possible when you were drinking, which they did.

I felt alone, isolated from society, frustrated, and angry at you. As your drinking continued, I knew I was beginning to lose my own sanity. I was exhausted and living with fear and worrying constantly while trying to work and pay the bills and be a father and mother to our boys was taking its toll on me.

You could not see this. You were not in a fit state to recognise anything that was going on around you, and it broke my heart to watch you killing yourself with drink. I had to do something; to reach out to someone who could help me.

So I got a number for Alanon and started to attend the meetings.'

I had known my husband was attending Alanon both in my drinking days and in my early recovery and supported him in that.

'The people in Alanon were a tremendous help to me, Mary. They really understood my dilemma because they were also living with an alcoholic. We shared our feelings and worries, our despair at watching someone we loved destroying their life and causing so much pain to the family. It was like a weight lifted from me to be able to express myself, and my emotions, without judgement or criticism.

I was given suggestions and sound advice to help me to live in the environment at home then. I looked forward to going there simply to offload my grievances and concerns.'

As my husband talked, I listened silently without interrupting him. As he spoke about those times, I had flashbacks of him lifting his newspaper, taking the car keys and leaving the house, without a word to me. I never questioned where he was going. To be truthful, when I was drinking, I didn't care. It was a relief for me when he left. It made drinking easier. I didn't have to hide it. The boys were always in their rooms by that stage, except to come down for something to eat. Most of the time, I would be passed out in bed by then.

My husband continued, 'I was advised to get away from you as much as possible, even for a couple of hours a day. So, I would take my paper and go to McDonald's for a coffee. That too helped me to regain some head peace, to regain the energy I needed to sustain my sanity while living with you in alcoholism.'

The worst part of it all for me was your complete ignorance and trying to stay calm and open minded. I kept telling myself that this was not the real you, but it was not easy, and I believe If I did not have the fellowship of Alanon to help me, I would have gone insane myself.

I could not face putting you out of our home and, thankfully, it didn't come to that. I knew, though, that if things didn't change, if you continued to drink this way, that the day would come when I would have to remove you from our home; both for me and the boys, and I hoped and prayed with all my heart that you would try to stop drinking before that day came.'

My husband became melancholy and paused for a few moments.

I waited in silence.

'You know,' he said then with sadness in his eyes. 'I couldn't even think about losing Danny when you were in that state. I couldn't face my pain of losing my son. There was no room in my mind for my grief. I was scared to grieve. I was worried that it would put me over the edge, that I would have a nervous breakdown, and then who would our boys have? So, I parked my grief at the back of my mind. Now I find it hard to bring it to the fore. I can only let myself feel a little at a time. It's too hard for me still.'

When Dessie shared this news with me, the tears fell silently from my eyes. The reality of the torture I had put this wonderful man through hit me hard.

I whispered, 'I'm so sorry, love.'

He nodded, smiling. 'It's okay, Mary. You are back now, and that's the main thing. You know,' he began again. 'That day you told me you wanted to stop was my rainbow moment. I felt a huge weight being lifted from me with those words, even though I knew it would be a rough time ahead. I was relieved that you could finally see what you were doing to yourself because nobody could get through to you.'

We paused here for another coffee, and when we sat down again, my husband asked me, 'What was the turning point for you, Mary? Why did you decide at that moment to try to stop?'

I sighed and reflected for a moment. 'I think,' I said. 'That particular day, as I lay in bed shaking and weak, I came to a place of hopelessness, Dessie. I saw the reality in my mind of what I had become, and it frightened me. At that moment, the clarity of my pitiful state of existence slammed into my brain and with it came a complete surrender. I gave up the fight, the insane notion that I could keep drinking like this and someday be normal again.'

My husband listened intently. We stared at each other in silence for a moment, both in a reflective mood.

'Did you believe I could stop?' I said to him suddenly.

He sighed in thought. 'I believed you had the strength, but I wasn't sure whether you had the will. I knew you were suffering over Danny's death as well. I was worried, but I tried not to think the worst. I was happy you had made the decision to try.

That first year when you came home from the treatment centre, I was very proud of you. You had transformed. The boys saw it too. They would say to me often, "Dad, isn't Mam doing great?" they were proud of you too.'

My eyes welled up with these words.

'I could exhale at last,' he said loudly. Then, he paused again, and his voice became sad. 'That's why when you started drinking again, it was devastating for me. I'd thought we were going to be okay as a family again, you know?' He looked at me for a moment.

I nodded solemnly.

'I also knew what lay ahead for the boys and me if you kept drinking,' Dessie continued to say. 'It was even worse for us the second time around because of that knowledge, but I had faith in you. I knew you could get sober again. I also knew that there was nothing I could do about it, except hope and pray that you would stop again soon, and you did.'

My husband took my hand in his. 'I know the battles you fought, Mary. I could see the pain in your eyes every day.'

'And I saw yours too, Dessie,' I replied. 'The difference was you were forced to live in my hell. That was cruel of me, but the Mary you knew had gone and, in her place, the alcoholic beast which emerged took over. I had no control by then once alcohol passed my lips. I'm so grateful you hung in there with me.'

'Me too.' He smiled.

'Tell me,' I said to him. 'Do you worry any more that I may drink again?'

'No,' he said immediately.

I was taken aback at his quick response.

'What is the point in worrying about something I have no control over? My life is relaxed, content, and peaceful now. The boys' lives are the same. One good thing that came out of that traumatic time is that now I appreciate and am so grateful for the simple things in life, the things that I used to take for granted.'

'Like what?' I asked humbly.

'Like a smile on your child's face,' Dessie answered. 'Or laughter in your home and a content state of mind. These things are precious to the boys and me now because we know what it's like to lose them.'

I bent my head in shame. To think that I had caused so much pain to the ones I loved most in the world by my drinking was almost too much to bear, but with humility, I needed to hear all this. I needed to be absolutely aware of what the circumstances would be both for my precious family and for me. All this information strengthened my resolve to stay sober.

My husband sensed how his words had impacted me and asked me was I okay.

'Yes, I'm fine,' I replied. 'Don't feel bad for telling the truth, Dessie. It's good that I know.'

He nodded. 'Well,' he said. 'Here is more truth for you, Mary. What happened to you, me, and the boys, both with Danny's death and your drinking, has changed me too; not in a bad way, but in a positive way.'

I looked at him curiously. 'How is that?' I said.

'Well,' he replied. 'I see a different you now, different even to what you were like before the drinking. You're more calm and easy going. You don't get in a state of panic like you used to, and you look on the bright side, telling me that worry is a waste of precious head space. You know the way I would always worry and huff and puff over everything.'

I smiled at him in response.

'Yes, well,' he said. 'I see all that now. I see how useless it is to worry about what may be. Danny's death is the main reason for that, but witnessing you being grateful and taking things in your stride has helped me to look at life in this way too. I never used to do that. It feels good not to worry all the time, so it's not all bad, Mary. The past is the past. I'm happy to leave it there.'

'Me too,' I said.

As I briefly mentioned earlier, my sons Ryan and Liam lived a constant state of worry and frustration, especially during the years from 2011 through to 2014 when my drinking had been at its most destructive. They had their world torn apart, and I could never completely mend the trauma they suffered by apologising.

For the most part of those horrendous years, they'd isolated themselves from me, with the advice of their father, which I am grateful for. We lived separately in our home. They spent most of their time in their rooms or at friends' homes. I was in such a savage state of mind as a result of my drinking day and night that I didn't care where my boys were.

I had lost all my emotional attachments to everybody. My brain was drowned in an alcoholic haze, affecting every cell, and turning me into a complete zombie. It stripped my mental state of any rational, decent or moral thinking patterns. I was completely enslaved to alcohol.

While in the process of writing this memoir, I thought perhaps I should ask them if they wished to talk about what they had suffered at the hands of the monster I had replaced their mother with, while I had been drinking alcoholically.

When I approached them about this, they shook their heads. I did not press them on the subject. I respected their wishes. They clearly did not feel the time was right for them to open up old wounds. Whatever demons they needed to face as a result of what they suffered by my drinking, can only be addressed when they feel comfortable to do so, and I will be by their sides to help in any way I can with humility.

I don't have the right or the skills to open something up in them, which they are not yet ready to reveal. Today there is much laughter in our home once more. Right now, for them, what happened in the past has been left there.

My life is simple today. I try to focus on what is going on now, rather than what may lie ahead. I don't dwell on the past anymore, either. What's done is done!

Like the Phoenix, I have risen from those ashes. Second to my sobriety, my family are what is most important to me. My sons are thriving. They are two bright, beautiful young men, both inside and out. They are my world, and we share a wonderful relationship, better than ever before.

My husband and I have a much better understanding of each other now also, which makes our home life serene and peaceful. I am eternally grateful for the unconditional love bestowed onto me. I am eternally grateful for my sobriety.

Never a day goes by that I don't grieve for my son Danny boy. Some days still, that despair and hopelessness crash down on me when I see his beautiful blue eyes smiling at me in my mind's eye. I miss what was and what life would have been if he were here on earth with us, but in death, we are given no choices.

I am a grieving mother. I always will be so, but I know with all my heart that my son's spirit shines in our hearts and our home every day. His light keeps us shining when the dark clouds appear. He keeps us smiling on. HE IS OUR RAINBOW.

THE END

My son's farewell

I lay in bed on a nameless night, restless, my emotions in turmoil. It had been several months since Danny had left us in this world. Sleep eventually came upon me and as I fell into deeper sleep I began to awaken in my subconscious. I found myself standing alone at the entrance of a long corridor. I stood there silently unafraid but apprehensive. The corridor was dimly lit, it beckoned me to move forward, which I did step by step slowly.

As I walked, I glanced to my left and to my right, there were small cubicles on either side of this corridor with curtains pulled around them, very similar to an accident and emergency room in hospitals. I could hear voices coming from these cubicles but could not make out the words been spoken, I kept moving forward. Suddenly I found myself standing in a small room, I looked around with a sense of recognition, and I knew this room! I had been here before! It was my Nanas little dining room at the back of her home.

I began to familiarise myself with my surroundings, I had spent many hours in this humble little room in my childhood. A sense of confusion came upon me. How could I be here I wondered, this room had been demolished over a decade ago when my brother and his wife bought my Nanas home and renovated it to suit their needs, for their future life together. I pondered on this and as I looked around at the familiar setting, the old sideboard, the small round table and battered old dining chairs, I Suddenly felt a presence to my left, I looked up to see my son Danny standing at the door of the room.

He came in and sat on one of the chairs at the table, I slowly walked to the table and sat opposite him, I was taken aback but not shocked. A feeling of relief I suppose came over me, this was because of the way my child looked. He was radiant and healthy. In the last few weeks before his death he was frail, thin and in a coma, a shell of the big boisterous healthy child he had been previous to his abrupt illness and his eyes shone beautiful brightly blue. I sat silently stunned for a moment.

Danny began to speak that kept me rooted in silence also, my son had lost his speech several weeks before his death due to a massive seizure he suffered, and he never regained his speech.

"Hello mam," my son said in a soft calm voice. I was held back from rushing to my child and taking him into my arms, not physically. There seemed to be an invisible barrier between us and I somehow instinctively knew I must not reach out to him nor did he make any gesture to come to me, which he often did at home. He would come to me in the kitchen and wrap his arms around my waist regularly but there, then he sat poised and calm he seemed almost matured for his young eight years.

Unfortunately, I cannot recall all that was spoken between us there in my Nanas old dining room, I do remember asking him over and over was he okay, how did he feel, to which he answered, I'm fine mam I'm fine. Danny then said in an almost pitying voice, "mam I can't go back with you.' When he said this I suddenly became overwhelmed with love and pity for my child, I instinctively knew in that moment that he was sad for me, that he was torn between wanting to be with me and knowing he had to go to where he needed to go.

As that awareness hit me, I knew what I had to do. I simply had to relieve my child's concern and worries for leaving us. I held back my emotions to let him see that I was not distressed. My son needed my help now, I could not do anything to help him in the last few weeks of his life on the earth, but there then I could, and I would.

Danny spoke again then, "mam" he said, "he won't let me go with you, he wants me", "and I have to go to him." My son did not utter these words in a despairing voice, nor did he show any fear, rather he spoke matter of factly, calmly. I remember in that moment taking in a deep breath, being very aware that I had to seem calm also and be the mother he needed me to be right there and then, I had to give him my permission and blessing to leave me, show him that I was okay. I sat back and looked into his eyes. "Danny boy," I said keeping my voice cheerful, "it's okay son, you go, I'm fine son, it's okay to go," Danny replied almost urgently, "he's calling me mam, I have to go." "Go Danny," I said, "go son, we will be fine." I fought tears back then and said almost in a whisper, "bye bye son..." I awoke immediately after I uttered those words on my pillow in the darkness of my bedroom.

The only emotion I recall having was one of immense gratitude simply because I was given that opportunity to see my child again, to hear his voice, to see him so perfectly healthy and glowing robust and beautiful, on his journey to eternity...

Our beautiful son,
DANNY BOY xxx
2001 - 2010

Acknowledgements

I would like to express my heartfelt gratitude to the family and friends who have helped me during this journey, especially my husband and sons. You've been the wind in my sails xxx.

A special thank you to Cala for your kindness and also my beautiful grandniece Cara.